RETURN TO WALLABY CREEK

Dev Masters obviously despised the fact
that Raina was an urban socialite who
had been a virtual stranger to her now
dead father, but nevertheless he was the
man she wanted to help her keep the
homestead intact ... she needed him as
her husband.

RETURN TO
WALLABY CREEK

BY
KERRY ALLYNE

MILLS & BOON LIMITED
15–16 BROOK'S MEWS
LONDON W1A 1DR

First published in Great Britain 1985
by Mills & Boon Limited

© Kerry Allyne 1985

Australian copyright 1985
Philippine copyright 1985
This edition 1985

ISBN 0 263 75200 3

Set in Monophoto Times 10 on 11 pt.
01–1185 – 55312

Made and printed in Great Britain by
Richard Clay (The Chaucer Press) Ltd,
Bungay, Suffolk

CHAPTER ONE

SHADES of amazement, not to mention some little dismay, were evident in Raina Cameron's deep blue eyes as she lifted them from the telegram in her hand to gaze agitatedly at her mother, Eve, and her stepfather, Michael Halliday.

'Why on earth didn't you get in touch with me when this first arrived?' she half questioned, half accused. 'You could have contacted me at Rottnest.' That being a popular island resort just off the coast from Perth in the State of Western Australia. 'Now there's been a full day wasted and it will probably be impossible for me to get up there in time.'

Resting on a comfortably cushioned lounger on a terrace that overlooked the brightly sparkling waters of the Swan River, Eve Halliday gave an eloquent shrug. 'It never occurred to me you would want to go.'

'To my own father's funeral?' Raina's finely marked brows rose expressively.

'Well, you could hardly say he's done much to warrant the title ... or your sudden, seeming allegiance,' her mother replied in pungent accents. 'After all, he made it plain enough he neither wanted to see, or have anything to do with you—or even any of the other members of his family, if it comes to that— from the time he and I were divorced some sixteen years ago. Since then you've seen him how many times? The grand total of once?' Her brown eyes widened sardonically. 'While even when we *were* married, you know as well as I do that he wasn't the slightest bit interested in his daughter. *Male* heirs w-were all he ever wanted!'

5

Knowing the reason for that brief falter, Raina sighed and watched as her stepfather leant across from his own lounger to touch his wife's arm comfortingly. 'Now, Eve, don't upset yourself,' he urged. 'That was a long time ago and you have Glen now, remember?'

He was meaning her young half-brother as a replacement for her mother and father's second child, Clark, who had met a tragic death at the untimely age of two when he'd wandered into the cattle yards and been kicked. An accident that had been the last straw as far as her mother was concerned for sharing a life with her first husband in the far northern Kimberley region of the State, Raina mused. While as for what her mother had just said about her father's attitude towards herself ... well, how could she dispute it? He *had* always made it abundantly, painfully, obvious that she came a poor second to her brother, and yet strangely, in spite of all that ...

'He was still my father when all's said and done, and I think at least one of us should attend if at all possible,' she proposed quietly. Not surprisingly, perhaps, in view of the circumstances, it was more than apparent her mother had no intention of doing so, not even for the sake of appearances. 'Besides, presuming they've been advised too, I'm sure Aunt Olivia and my cousins will all be there ... if only to protect their interests in the property,' she inserted wryly, 'and it wouldn't exactly look good if I was the only one who couldn't be bothered to make the effort.'

'Although it would be perfectly understandable,' Eve insisted, recovered now. Then, after pausing thoughtfully for a moment, went on negligently, 'In any case, now that Hayes, the main and just about sole vote advocating retention of the property and the continuation of the Estate as a whole, has gone, there's nothing to stop both properties being sold and the other assets being realised as well ... and for that neither you nor Olivia, or any of the others, need be present at the reading of your father's will. All that's required is for you all to formally advise Charley Lawrence, Hayes's solicitor, that you wish the Estate wound up and the proceeds therefrom duly distributed.'

'No reason, that is, apart from the small matter of paying one's last respects, of course,' Raina put forward somewhat ironically.

Her mother gave a decidedly cynical snort. 'Respects? You as good as said yourself that the only thing Olivia and the rest of your cousins respect is the money! So if they do attend the funeral, it certainly won't be out of respect for Hayes, I can assure you! Not that I blame them, mind you! How could anyone possibly respect a man who ignored his own child as your father did you? Not to mention refusing to have any of his other relatives even setting foot on the place either!' She took a deep breath, eyeing her daughter a little incredulously. 'Moreover, I must admit that I find the idea of you, of all people, abruptly considering paying him *your* respects totally incomprehensible!'

Raina hunched a slender, golden-toned shoulder and partly turned away to stare out over the river. 'It was only an expression,' she sighed. If the truth were known her feelings towards her father at the moment were a little confused. The telegram advising of his unexpected death had certainly shocked her, but except for that nothing else really seemed to have changed, and in a way that depressed her. She felt some other emotions should have manifested themselves—sadness, regret— or even a diminishing of the pain, the disappointment, the niggling resentment at her father's complete rejection of her all these years at least now that he was dead, but as yet none of those things had occurred. There was only an increasing sense of obligation to

attend his funeral ... as if to prove she hadn't turned
her back on him in death as he had on her in life? she
wondered ruefully. Nevertheless, having made up her
mind, she now swung back to her mother and
stepfather decisively.

'Well, whether any respects, as such, are due or not, I
do still plan to fly up there for the funeral,' she advised.
'Though lord knows if I'll be able to make it in time at
this late date. It's being held tomorrow morning I think
the wire said.' She glanced down at the telegram in her
hand once more, scanning the stark words more
thoroughly this time.

It advised:

'REGRET TO INFORM YOU YOUR FATHER
FATALLY INJURED IN RIDING ACCIDENT
MONDAY   STOP   FUNERAL   11.30AM
WEDNESDAY 8TH WALLABY CREEK IF
INTERESTED ... MASTERS'

Once having re-read it and confirmed the time,
however, Raina found her gaze drawn to the last couple
of words again. And just what was that 'if interested'
supposed to imply? she frowned in no little indignation.
It seemed to her there was a rather caustic ring about it
and, as a result, she took exception immediately. How
dare this 'Masters' person presume to add such a
remark!

'So just who is this Masters who sent this?' she
looked up to enquire tightly. 'One of Charley
Lawrence's employees?'

With a shake of his head to indicate his lack of
knowledge, Michael Halliday left it to his wife to shed
whatever light she could on the matter. Which was
exactly zero, Raina soon discovered as her parent
displayed her ignorance with a shrug.

'How should I know?' Eve countered indifferently,

the whole matter evidently of little interest to her anyway. 'Since I married Michael I haven't even been a beneficiary from the Estate, so you're more likely to know who's been dealing with it than I am.'

'Hmm . . .' Raina pressed her lips together vexedly as she turned for the house, intent on ringing the airline office, and trying to recall the name as she went, but couldn't. Whoever he was he sounded as autocratic as his name, she decided tartly, and resolved to inform him in no uncertain terms when she did finally discover his identity that such comments were none of his business to make!

Fortunately for Raina she was able to get a cancellation on the 6.00 a.m. non-stop flight from Perth to the northern coastal town of Derby some sixteen hundred miles distant, and from where she had also managed to obtain a seat in a charter plane that would take her the further six hundred miles inland to Wallaby Creek on its way through to Kununurra. Even so, she was only too aware that her schedule left no room for any time loss if she was to make it by eleven-thirty and, in consequence, as the Fellowship F28 took off in the early hours of the following morning on the first leg of her journey she was nowhere near as relaxed as she might have been.

Some considerable time spent looking out of the window instead of reading the book she had bought at the airport did help to allay her anxieties to some extent—the rate at which they were passing over the ground below gave the comforting impression of urgent speed at least—and for a while she watched with interest as the closer settled farming lands gave way to a mat of grey bush, to mulga scrub and bare claypans, spinifex covered ranges broken by spectacular red gorges rimmed with the dark green of trees. There were

rivers—flowing again now after the recent wet season—
lined with stately old river red gums, the yellow of far-
reaching desert, and as they at last neared their
destination the curve of the shoreline away to their left
and the glint of an aquamarine sea.

Derby, at the head of King Sound, was an oasis of
buildings built on a point of flat land that jutted into
tidal marshes that, from the air, formed incredible fern-
like mosaics along their many channels, and where
ships tied up at the jetty became stranded on the mud
until the sea returned due to the great tidal variations.

However, as the plane began its descent Raina was
more concerned with time now than she was with the
view outside because, to her dismay, the umpteenth
check of her watch since leaving Perth showed that it
was nearly nine. They were ten minutes late and
although, under other circumstances, she wouldn't have
considered that worth commenting upon, with such a
tight timetable as hers was today, every minute lost
increased her chances of being late.

With this in mind, she therefore did her best to
ensure she was among the first to leave the aircraft and
hurried across to the terminal intent on locating the
pilot who was to transport her the rest of the way, and
ignoring the unexpected heat that assailed her on
stepping on to the tarmac. Being ready to leave himself,
it transpired that the pilot was looking for her too, so
luckily their meeting was achieved without too much
delay, and although there were some impatient minutes
spent by Raina as she waited for her single piece of
luggage to be off-loaded from the jet, all in all she was
back in the air, though in a considerably smaller Cessna
on this occasion, before too great a time had elapsed.

'So you'd be old Hayes's daughter, would you?'
Davey Newell, the clean-cut young pilot turned to
query once they were heading in an easterly direction.

Seated next to him since she was the only passenger—
he mostly only carried goods, she had been informed—
Raina's return gaze carried a touch of surprise. 'Well,
yes, but how did you know? Because of the name?'

'Partly,' he agreed, his mouth beginning to twist
wryly. 'But mainly because just about everyone up here
knows he had a daughter living in Perth and, what with
the funeral and all, this is the most logical route from
there.'

'I see,' she nodded, wondering just what else
everyone in the area seemingly knew about her family's
affairs.

'I also heard there was another group who arrived
yesterday afternoon from Darwin,' he continued
expansively. 'More relatives?'

'Probably my aunt and cousins,' she surmised,
guessing that it would have been more convenient for
the other family members who either lived in Adelaide
or Sydney to fly to Darwin and then journey south.
There was a slight pause during which she smoothed
out some imaginary wrinkles in her slim-fitting, black
skirt. 'You knew my father, then?'

'Not what you'd call really well, although I had met
him a few times,' he relayed. 'But then everyone up here
knows everyone else to some extent or another.' He
paused, his expression becoming sympathetic. 'We were
all sorry to hear about his death. It must have come as
quite a shock to you, happening so unexpectedly.'

'Yes, it did,' Raina acceded pensively, wishing the
reason for her return to Wallaby Creek could have been
a happier one.

Davey swept her lightly tanned features with a
considering glance, noting the sleek fall of shoulder
length, russet brown hair, the darkly lashed blue eyes
above an attractively retroussé nose, the generously
wide and curving mouth.

'You look a little like him, you know . . . only much prettier, of course,' he complimented with a smile.

'Thank you.' Shining white teeth made an appearance in a brief responding laugh before her face sobered again. 'Do I really take after him, though?'

He looked at her strangely. 'Don't you know?'

Regretting the spontaneous question, Raina averted her gaze swiftly. 'No, not really,' she admitted in a small voice. But on reminding herself whose fault that was, added in a rather more challenging tone, 'I was only six when I left Alliance, you know, my father's property, and except for one short visit he paid my mother and myself when I was eleven I never saw him again, so I'm afraid the few recollections I do have of him are decidedly hazy.'

'Oh!' For a second or two Davey looked a little disconcerted and then he passed the moment off with another smile. 'Well then, since you asked, yes, your hair and eyes are much the same colour as his were. You're also tall like he was, and you've got the same shaped jaw.'

'A regular little chip off the old block, no less,' she quipped facetiously in an effort to disguise the sudden hurt the comparison had engendered. If they had been that similar in feature, wasn't it possible they could also have been alike in other ways too . . . if her father had cared sufficiently to look? But having invited the comments, she now tried to steer the conversation away from anything so personal. 'And—and this riding accident he was involved in. Would you happen to know just what occurred? Like most telegrams, the one I received was very sparse in its details, I'm afraid.'

'Yes—well—as I heard it, he was out with some of his men early on Monday and his mount lost its footing going down some hill or the other and Hayes, in one of those freak instances that happen at times, just had the bad luck to strike his head on a rock as they came down.' He expelled a long, heavy breath. 'Death was instantaneous, apparently.'

Raina acknowledged the information with a sadly understanding nod. She supposed there was always the chance of something similar occurring whenever there was a lot of riding done in rough country. However, mention of the telegram, plus an earlier statement of Davey's, did bring to mind another matter she was restively waiting to have solved.

'While we're on the subject of the telegram, though, and as you said everyone more or less knows everyone else in the region,' she began as impassively as possible, 'would you also happen to know anyone by the name of Masters, by any chance?'

'You mean, Dev Masters?'

'I wouldn't know. There was only a surname on the telegram.'

'Yes, then that'd be Dev all right,' he declared confidently. 'He's the manager over at Ajax Downs, the station next door to Alliance. He's a good bloke, and he and your Dad always got on real well together.'

Something Raina could well believe judging by the tone of his telegram! 'But why would the manager of another property be forwarding such information to the members of the Cameron Estate? Surely that's the prerogative of Charley Lawrence, my father's solicitor.'

'I wouldn't know about that,' shrugged Davey. 'You'd do better asking Charley that kind of thing when you see him.'

And so she very definitely would! promised Raina to herself. As far as she was concerned those last two words in the message were completely inexcusable whether the writer was an old crony of her father's or not!

For the next hour or so Davey spent most of the

time indicating points of interest along their route; the rugged, water-filled gorges that were such an outstanding feature of the Kimberleys, the pindan areas of the desert margins, the spear grass plains, and the flat-topped ranges etched in rose and purple, rust and yellow.

In places it was a sun-dried, harsh landscape, but possessing its own savage, awesome beauty for all that, while in others golden, park-like savannah lands dotted with bauhinias, squat boabs and white gums swept majestically away into the distance, interrupted only by straight-topped and steep-sloping solitary island masses of rock mantled with spinifex.

There was a feeling of immense space about it all, of timelessness, of a vivid blue infinity of sky, and it brought with it slowly awakening memories on Raina's part from her long-forgotten childhood that evoked strange emotions within her. It was as if the images her mind was conjuring up were designed to remind her that this was her birthplace, she mused, and then dismissed the idea as illogical. It was a little foolish to be thinking in such a vein when the family property would most likely be sold within the very near future.

Returning her thoughts to the immediate, she asked of Davey, 'Is it much further?' They had already passed one little settlement but as yet there was still no sign of another that she could see.

'Mmm, just a bit,' he returned almost apologetically, and she sighed, knowing an arrival before eleven-thirty was out of the question. Now it was simply a matter of discovering by just how much she was going to be late. 'But there's always the chance they won't start on time,' he went on to add in a more encouraging tone. 'Especially in view of the number likely to be present.'

'Oh?' She sent him a surprised glance. 'I imagined it would be a rather small affair.'

'I'd be amazed if it was. After all, there's been Camerons in these parts since just after the turn of the century, and apart from being known to one and all, Hayes was also very well liked and respected. I probably would have attended myself if this stuff,' nodding towards the cartons and packages behind them, 'hadn't been required urgently. He's given me a fair bit of business since I started up a couple of years ago.'

This information perhaps came as more of a surprise to Raina than the other had. Since his family hadn't been on particularly good terms with her father, she had always assumed that others would have found him equally difficult and unsociable as well. But then, the slightly piqued thought followed, it had been he who had flatly refused to have anything to do with his family, not the other way around. Unlike his neighbours and friends, apparently, they hadn't been considered worthy of his regard or association!

Eventually, however, the small township of Wallaby Creek—it only had a few hundred population—did at last come into view, but twenty minutes late, and as Davey brought the plane to a halt on the airstrip that was within walking distance of the main street, both he and Raina alighted quickly.

'You go on. I'll take your case over to the hotel for you,' he offered helpfully.

'Thank you, I'd really appreciate that.' Her accompanying smile was sincere. 'And thank you also for such an informative trip.' Pausing momentarily, she glanced about her anxiously. 'Er—just whereabouts is the church?' Although she knew she had visited the town as a child, unfortunately nothing seemed familiar.

'That's it over there.' He pointed out a narrow, white painted, wooden building some way down on the other side of the main street. 'Although it looks as if they've left there by now. Maybe you'd better go straight to the cemetery instead.'

'And that's . . . where? Behind the church?'

'Sort of,' he half grinned obliquely. 'Just turn right at the church and you'll see the creek a little way behind it. Follow that and it'll lead you right there.'

'Thank you,' she said again, beginning to walk away.

'I hope you're not too late, and if you're going to be around for a while perhaps I could see you again,' he called after her hopefully.

Raina swung back to send him a regretful smile. 'I'd like that, but unfortunately I only anticipate being here a couple of days at the most.'

'That's too bad.' He both sounded and looked disappointed.

She nodded expressively but had no choice but to continue on her way. Although she appreciated Davey's interest, she couldn't afford to be any later than she was already!

Once across the bitumened main street, Raina broke into a part fast walk, part run until she rounded the church and then had to slow her steps considerably on finding the rest of the way consisted of an unsealed track that definitely wasn't conducive to any speed in her city designed high-heeled shoes. She was also conscious of beads of perspiration starting to form at her temples—the steadily climbing temperature was even more noticeable here than it had been in Derby— and if she hadn't thought her vividly white silk blouse not quite sombre enough for the occasion, she would willingly have removed the smartly cut jacket she was wearing over it that matched her black skirt.

At another time, and in other footwear, Raina speculated that she probably would have enjoyed the walk beneath the shady gums that lined the clear, wide creek that gave the town its name, but as it was she couldn't take time to appreciate it greatly, and all too soon she had to leave the welcome shade again in order to make her way past a great number of vehicles parked outside the iron railing, bounded cemetery in which only a single coolibah grew, and beneath which a minister of the church was conducting the service before a surprisingly large number of mourners.

The rusty old gate leading into the humble burial ground squeaked shrilly in protest as Raina pushed it open, causing just about every eye to swing in her direction for a second, and bringing a flush of embarrassment to her already warm cheeks as she joined the congregation at the graveside. Mostly they were men, she noted before bowing her head respectfully. Tall, thick-set men, uniformly bronzed to shades of mahogany by years spent working beneath a relentless sun, even a sprinkling of darker skinned aboriginal stockmen, but all of whom gave the impression they would have felt more at ease with their wide brimmed hats on their heads instead of in their hands.

In the main, the few quietly dressed women present appeared to be grazier's wives—except for her own rather more extravagantly outfitted relatives, that was, Raina amended drily on realising that they were indeed all in attendance. Her aunt seemed to be wearing every piece of jewellery she possessed, while her two female cousins, although certainly less ornamented, still managed to stand out from the crowd with their colourful, high fashion creations and elaborate applications of make-up. The two males of the group fitting in decidedly better in dark, if obviously expensive suits.

For the remainder of the service Raina kept her head deferentially low, trying to concentrate her thoughts on the man who had been her father, but finding it difficult to grieve deeply over the passing of someone she could only faintly remember and who had shown only too clearly that she had meant nothing to him. There was merely a feeling of regret for the way things had turned out.

Towards the end there was one disturbance that temporarily distracted her, however. A flock of noisy corellas suddenly came to rest in one of the trees edging the creek, their raucous squawking nearly drowning out the minister's words, and bringing a half smile of recollection to her soft lips as she glanced involuntarily in their direction. She could remember many such flocks as this turning trees white with their numbers in days long past. Then just as swiftly as they had arrived, the parrots abruptly took to the air again and headed out across the undulating landscape.

Raina's gaze followed them for a short distance and then became focussed musingly on the earth itself, noting its richly red colour and its wet season's growth of grass already beginning to turn yellow beneath the hotly blazing sun as she slowly brought her glance back to her immediate surroundings.

In the process her gaze passed over her relatives standing next to white haired, kindly featured Charley Lawrence who had been managing the legal side of her father's affairs for as long as she could remember and whom she knew very well since it was he who presented the accountant's reports concerning Alliance at the Estate's general meetings in Perth each year. Then her scanning glance came to a sudden, surprised halt on connecting with a distinctly unfavourable and narrowed look from a man of some thirty-one or two years who stood on Charley's far side.

Just who he was Raina had no idea, although she suspected the deeply tanned hue of his strong-boned face proclaimed him a local despite the obviously city style of his attire that couldn't disguise the width of his heavily muscular shoulders. His dark hair shone in the morning sun and was inclined to curl, his deep brown eyes with their etching of fine lines at the corners appearing almost as black as the thick, long lashes that framed them. His nose was straightly sculptured, his mouth wide and firmly shaped, the corners attractively tilted. But it was the aggressively male set of his jaw that told most about him, she decided, for it seemed to denote unmistakably that here was a man, a real man, one to be taken into account, and certainly not one of the new marshmallow breed who became confused about their male identity through their desire to be laid-back and understanding. Nevertheless, or perhaps as a result of, her return stare was openly challenging to his continuing observation before she lowered her eyes to the grave in front of her once more in a deliberately leisurely gesture of disdainful dismissal. Whoever he was, he could keep his disapproving looks for those more ready to accept them!

Not long afterwards the minister finally brought the service to its conclusion and Raina very quickly became enveloped by her relatives.

'Oh, Raina, dear, what a tragedy for poor Hayes to go like that,' lamented her short and plump, china doll faced aunt as she dabbed ostentatiously at her eyes with a lace-edged handkerchief. 'I was so distressed when I received the news that I almost didn't think I would be able to come. I'm the only one of my generation left, you know, now that my poor baby brother's gone too.'

'Yes, I'm sure it came as a shock to all of us, Aunt Olivia,' Raina consoled, reflecting that Quint Cameron—her aunt's other brother, and father of her cousins Faith and Malcolm—who had been killed some years previously in a light plane crash, along with his wife, had died at a comparatively early age as well.

'I would have thought you could at least made

certain you arrived here in time for the whole service, though,' Olivia Hewitt went on to chide in disappointed tones. 'We had begun to think you didn't intend coming at all.'

Her niece's lips curved wryly. 'As it happens, I was lucky to get here when I did. I wasn't informed of what had happened until yesterday afternoon.'

'Yesterday afternoon?' her aunt echoed with a frown. 'But you were all notified on Monday.'

'Yes, well, so was I apparently, but I happened to have been spending a couple of days over at Rotto with a few friends and because Mum didn't think I would want to attend she unfortunately didn't bother contacting me but just left it until I arrived home yesterday instead.'

'Oh, how silly of her,' Olivia chattered, using her handkerchief as a hopefully cooling fan now. 'She should have known we would all want to come now that the Estate's going to be finalised.' Pausing, her expression became tinged with excitement. 'For myself, I've had such a wonderful idea. I think I might buy . . .'

'Yes, Mother, we all know what you're planning . . . at the moment,' her daughter broke in sardonically. Tall, glamorous, and totally sure of herself, three times married and divorced, Adele Radcliffe at thirty was almost the complete antithesis of her vacillating and somewhat feather-brained parent.

'But Raina doesn't,' Olivia complained in an aggrieved manner. And moving closer to the younger girl confided in a thrilled voice, 'I'm thinking of buying myself a plane with my proceeds from the Estate.'

'A plane!' It was Raina's turn to repeat now in astonishment, her blue eyes widening. 'Whatever for?'

Her aunt appeared hurt by her obvious lack of appreciation for the idea. 'Because it would be *so* much more convenient when my friends and I wish to go visiting outside Adelaide, of course,' she explained as if it was the most natural thing in the world for her to want. 'After all, some of our friends live miles and miles away from the nearest airport, and just think . . .'

'Oh, not now, Mother, not now,' Adele broke in on her again impatiently. 'There's people here waiting to express their sympathies to Raina before the rest of us retire to the hall for some refreshments, and the sooner it's concluded the sooner we can get out of this infernal sun!' She grimaced expressively.

Adele proved to be right and very shortly all of them, though more so Raina and her aunt—still remembered by a considerable number of the older inhabitants of the region from the time when she too had lived on the family property until her late teens—were busy accepting condolences on their loss, and expressing their own appreciation in return not only for the thoughts but also the great distances many of those present had travelled in order to pay their respects.

Towards the last, the small group of aboriginal stockmen who had been waiting patiently for the crowd to diminish, began to make their way over to where Raina was standing, the eldest of them, a white haired man in his fifties, taking the lead as they neared her. There was something about him that immediately struck a chord in the depths of Raina's memory and she struggled hard, but unsuccessfully, to force remembrance into coming.

'You not remember me, Miss Raina,' he surmised with a shy half smile on reaching her, his hands fidgeting with the battered bush hat held in front of him.

She had no option but to shake her head apologetically. 'Not your name, no, I'm sorry, although I do . . .' She halted abruptly as from out of the blue the name she had been seeking all at once flashed into her

mind. 'Yes, I do, you're Daniel, aren't you? Daniel . . .
Daniel Jimari! My father's head stockman,' she recalled
happily.

He nodded with obvious pleasure that she had
remembered after all. 'Mmm, me and Ngarla we've
been with Hayes ever since we all piccaninnies together.
We've never wanted to work anywhere else.'

Ngarla! How many years was it since she had heard
that name? Raina fell to musing. And yet how many
times had she herself used it when she had been living
on the property and had deliberately entered Daniel's
wife's domain, the kitchen, in search of whatever tasty
tidbits she could cajole rounded, motherly Ngarla into
giving her. Not that she had ever had to use much
persuasion, she recollected, for her father's cook and
housekeeper had always been more than willing to hand
over a sample of her justly renowned baking.

'And how is Ngarla . . . well?' she brought her
thoughts back to the present to ask interestedly. 'You
both are?' Her winged brows lifted enquiringly.

'We be better if we not so old,' he joked, showing still
strong white teeth in a rueful grin. 'But Ngarla, she
sorry she not come today. She say more better only I
come. She see you bye-'m-bye when you visit Alliance,
okay?'

'Oh, but I . . .' Raina began and then came to a
sudden stop. Actually, she hadn't envisaged going out
to the property at all, but on thinking about it, why
shouldn't she? There was no reason why she couldn't
extend the length of her stay another day or so. 'Yes,
I'll see her when I visit Alliance,' she now agreed on a
decisive note. 'I'll look forward to it.' Looking past him
she smiled at his companions who were standing to one
side, and then glanced back at Daniel. 'And these are
some of the other stockmen from Alliance, are they?'

'Yes'm,' he nodded, and signalling for them to come

forward introduced them one by one, each of them murmuring, if a little selfconsciously, suitable words of commiseration to her in turn. When they had finished, Daniel added some of his own. 'Your father, he a good boss . . . a good feller. We all sorry he gone now.' Pausing, he fiddled with his hat some more before continuing on a somewhat anxious note. 'You not going to sell Alliance now, are you, Miss Raina?'

Unable to hold his liquid dark and apprehensive gaze, Raina looked away uncomfortably. 'I'm afraid the decision isn't only mine to make, Daniel,' she advised, chewing at her lip.

'But you his daughter! Alliance belong to you now.'

'Only as a part shareholder, though. Besides, the property is only allowed to be run by a male member of the family,' she tried to explain as simply as possible some of the complicated legalities of the Estate.

From the furrowing of his brow it was evident he didn't understand—which really didn't surprise Raina in the least. The documents her grandfather and his brother had originally had drawn up to ensure the estate continued as they had wished it to *was* complex, and water-tight. As had been proved to her relatives' considerable annoyance in the past.

'But you got him . . . and him,' Daniel now motioned towards her cousin, Malcolm, and her cousin-in-law, Steven.

'Except that they're neither capable of managing Alliance, nor even interested in doing so, if it comes to that. They want it sold . . . as well as everything else the estate owns,' she had no choice but to reveal no matter how much it obviously amazed and disappointed the old man with her.

Daniel shook his head despondently and a few minutes later began to take his leave along with the other stockmen. Raina watched him go with her lower lip caught between pearly white teeth. She felt terrible at having had to destroy his hopes of the property remaining under Cameron control, but at the same time couldn't see what else she could have done. Surely it was better to have told him the truth than to have prevaricated and thereby given him false hopes?

With a sigh she turned to see if her aunt was ready to leave yet and once again found herself on the receiving end of a derogatorily contemptuous stare from the very same man who had raked her with such a hard-eyed look earlier. Only on this occasion he now began covering the distance between them with a purposeful, long-limbed stride.

'Couldn't wait to tell poor old, faithful Daniel the bad news, eh?' he immediately charged in scornful tones on coming to a halt a pace or two away and seeming to tower over her.

He was certainly tall, at least six foot two, Raina estimated inconsequentially before unconsciously squaring her shoulders and drawing herself up to her own full five foot six, refusing to be intimidated either by his size or his remark.

'I haven't the faintest idea what you're talking about,' she evaded at her haughtiest. Despite it being apparent he had somehow deduced the content of her conversation with Daniel she had no intention whatsoever of defending herself to him! 'Not that what I had to say to my father's head stockman is any business of yours in any case. So if you don't mind, I'll just say good day,' in dismissive tones, 'and find myself more congenial company.' She made to step past him.

'Yeah, it's always easy come, easy go, for the likes of you, isn't it?' His well-shaped mouth curved caustically.

Raina draw a deep, smouldering breath and spun to face him again. 'Look, I don't know who you are, but . . .'

'The name's Masters . . . Devlin Masters,' he supplied in a sardonic drawl. 'I run the property next to Alliance.'

So this was the person who had sent that sarcastic wire. She might have known! 'You also despatch extremely offensively worded telegrams, Mr Masters! But then, having now met you, I realise it wouldn't have been possible for you to do otherwise, because you're just downright offensive altogether!' she snapped acidly.

'Meaning, you find the truth unpalatable?' His brows rose goadingly. 'Perhaps it's just as well then that you don't mean to continue with the work Hayes, and his father before him, dedicated their lives to, because you could say bluntness of speech is a way of life up here. We call it as it is!'

'There's also some who confuse bluntness with rudeness!' she promptly sniped.

'But many more who equate it with honesty!'

'Although not in your case, I'm sure!'

'Why? Because I'm presumptuous enough to actually see you as you are . . . a self-centred socialite who doesn't give a damn about anything or anybody in the pursuit of your useless, parasitic existence?' he retorted scathingly.

Never having been spoken to in such a manner in her life before, Raina gasped incredulously, hardly knowing what to take him to task for first. 'How dare you call me a parasite!' she finally flared hotly.

'You figure you're not?' he countered, unperturbed. 'So tell me, just what do you do for a living, Miss Cameron?'

'I—I . . .' She faltered to a halt, uncertain as to how the conversation had become focussed on her lifestyle, and experiencing the discomfiting feeling that she was losing ground. 'That has nothing to do with it!' she denied, albeit not as convincingly as she would have liked.

'In other words, I'm right!' Masters gave no quarter. 'You live off the proceeds of other people's sweat while contributing absolutely nothing yourself!'

'Well, whether I do or not, it's no concern of yours!' she fumed. 'And thank you for being so understanding on the day of my father's funeral! Your compassion knows no bounds!'

'Oh, don't give me that!' A mirthless half laugh issued from his strong, darkly tanned throat. 'Everyone's well aware of just how much your father *didn't* mean to you. Why, you couldn't even put yourself out to the extent of arriving in time! And not only that but you seem to be forgetting I *saw* exactly how grief-stricken you were during the service. You were more interested in that mob of bloody parrots and in gazing around the countryside!'

'For reasons you couldn't even begin to guess at, you—you unfeeling ox!' she stormed, strangely feeling close to tears. His accusations were just so unfair! 'And—and if you *did* think so much of him, then, why was he buried here, in this almost derelict cemetery,' she accused irrationally, waving a hand to indicate the other, not always straight, headstones that were half concealed in the long grass, 'and not in Kununurra?'

'Because it was his wish to be buried here,' came the stony elucidation. 'As you too would have known if . . .'

'Oh, do come on, Raina!' Adele suddenly interrupted him by calling, and her cousin could have kissed her for providing her with an excuse to escape the objectionable Devlin Masters' company. 'We're ready to drive up to the hall for the refreshments the Ladies' Auxiliary have been kind enough to provide for us.'

'I'm coming,' Raina acknowledged in relief as she promptly set off towards the older girl without a backward look, her spirits already beginning to lift at the thought that that was the last she would be seeing of her father's neighbour.

'There's about a dozen of Hayes's closest friends coming back to the hall with us,' Adele continued as Raina reached her, gesturing to those mourners who hadn't as yet departed. 'Then afterwards, Dev's been an absolute darling and invited us all to stay the night at his property rather than at the hotel here in town. It will be much more comfortable, not to say private, than discussing Estate business in the bar of the hotel, don't you agree?'

No, of course she didn't! She was aghast at the prospect, if Adele did but know. 'Oh, but we couldn't possibly expect him to accommodate all of us on such short notice,' she put forward desperately.

'But it was he who offered,' shrugged Adele. Then leaning forward slightly, imparted with unmistakeable meaning, 'And I, for one, don't mind admitting that I'm quite looking forward to getting to know him better. He's my kind of man!'

'Quite possibly, but . . .'

'Oh, do stop trying to fault the plan, Raina!' Her cousin's voice sharpened impatiently. 'It was all arranged this morning before you arrived. All you have to do is go along with it.'

Because whatever Adele wanted, Adele always got? grimaced Raina, unable to think of a solitary thing her cousin had desired and been denied. And not doubting that this time would prove any different either since everyone else had apparently accepted the arrangement. She sighed. It seemed there was little she could do about it now but go along with it, as Adele suggested, and with as good a grace as possible—if only to show Devlin Masters that his opinions regarding herself were completely irrelevant as far as she was concerned.

CHAPTER TWO

WHILE at the hall, Raina was the recipient of more words and expressions of sympathy from those who hadn't previously extended them, but although they were all delivered pleasantly enough, she still thought she could detect some feelings of restraint, of reproval almost, among her father's oldest acquaintances.

She supposed it was their way of showing the dim view they had taken of her late arrival when everyone else had managed to get there in plenty of time, but as she didn't care to explain to one and all her mother's offhand treatment of the matter, she had no option but to allow their misassumptions to continue. Personally, and in view of her father's attitude towards her throughout her life, she was more inclined to think she had quite satisfactorily fulfilled her duty by even attending at all, but evidently those who had known him longer, and as a neighbour and friend, were of a different opinion.

After an hour or two, however, most of those present gradually began taking their leave. Some had a couple of hundred miles or more to cover before reaching home, others even longer who had flown their own planes, but all of them obviously preferred to return to their properties before nightfall.

As well as that, Raina and her relatives had some distance to go also before reaching Ajax Downs homestead, even though the station's boundaries did come to within twenty miles of Wallaby Creek, but when they all eventually took their seats in the station wagons belonging to Dev Masters and Charley

Lawrence—the latter having driven down from Kununurra—Raina made certain she travelled with her father's solicitor, along with her cousin, Faith, and her husband. Adele, of course, had equally made sure she gained the front passenger seat in Dev Masters' vehicle, leaving her mother and cousin, Malcolm, to occupy the rear, but the arrangement had suited Raina admirably. The less time she spent in company with Dev Masters the more relaxed she was.

Although the road through town was sealed, immediately they passed the last house so the bitumen disappeared too, as did any hopes of a particularly comfortable journey, for after the recent heavy rains the road had degenerated into a series of water-filled potholes and hardening ruts that wouldn't be levelled again until the surface had dried sufficiently for the graders to set to work making it reasonably traversable once more.

As it was, it made conversation relatively difficult for a lot of the time as they swerved around wash-aways, bounced through those potholes that were unavoidable, and rattled across already dried hoof marks of cattle that had crossed in the wet, but being of a determined, autocratic nature, thirty-six year old Faith Bramwell wasn't the type to allow anything so immaterial as a corrugated road deny her the opportunity of making her wishes known.

'Naturally you too will be agreeing to the sale of the Estate in its entirety now, Raina,' she began in her cool, decisive voice, taking acceptance for granted. 'The rest of us have already agreed that's what we all want, and what should be done.'

Thinking they might at least have waited to consult with her as well, Raina shrugged. 'I guess so,' she acceded, though in not nearly so resolved a tone.

'You *guess* so?' Faith fixed her with a censuring look.

'I suggest you be a little more positive than that because we're all hoping to have this matter settled tonight so we can return home tomorrow. After all, Steven,' nodding towards her lawyer husband in the front seat, 'is a very busy man with very important work to do. He can't afford to waste more time here than he has already, waiting for you to make up your mind.' She paused, patting into place her already tidy blonde hair. 'In any event, since you don't have a husband your vote really counts for very little because there isn't a male member of the family *to* run the property—the foremost obligation for the continuation of the Estate—so you may as well agree and be done with it.'

'But Union,' the family sheep property in the south of the State, 'has only had a manager, not a member of the family running it ever since Uncle Quint and Aunt Bridget died.' Raina felt entitled to remind, if a little perversely.

Her cousin's lips pursed with annoyance. 'Only because Hayes used to fly down there every few months to give instructions as to what was to be done on the place, and as a result could claim to be running both properties! If it had been at all possible we would have had the estate finalised then. Steven certainly looked into the matter, I can assure you, but unfortunately that was also a circumstance that had been provided for in the terms and there was nothing we could do about it! Happily, though, that doesn't apply any more.' Her expression assumed a decidedly pleased cast.

So it would appear to be all cut and dried, sighed Raina as she looked out on the vista of open plains they were passing, and which were intermittently dotted with giant termite mounds whose shadows striped the ground in the afternoon sun. Not that she really knew why she should care whether her vote counted for anything or not when she had been fully intending to

support the idea of a sale, anyway, when she left Perth
that morning. She was probably just being impulsively
sentimental because the property had been in Cameron
hands for so long, she decided, and swung back to face
her cousin with a studiously friendly smile on her lips.

'I suppose you've heard what Aunt Olivia's thinking
of buying if—when everything's finalised,' she remarked
on a wry note.

'Who hasn't!' The older woman's brows arched
explicitly. 'I've never heard anything more ridiculous,
or wasteful, in my life! She spends money like water,
and usually on the most useless and outlandish things
anyone could imagine, that I often think she shouldn't
be allowed out without a keeper . . . to protect her from
her own brainless decisions! It's just as well her last
husband left her extremely well provided for, otherwise
I've no doubt both she and Adele would be bankrupt
by now!'

Although she was willing to concede that most of
what her cousin had said was correct, Raina still felt
Faith to have been a little hard on their aunt. True, she
did waste a great deal of money, but at the same time she
was very generous with it too, as anyone who had taken
a hard luck story to her would have been able to verify.

'Oh, well, maybe Adele will be able to talk her out of
it,' she now suggested, starting to feel sorry she had
mentioned the subject. 'I don't think she's particularly
in favour of the idea.'

'Adele!' Faith exclaimed scornfully. 'Most times I
think she's almost as bad as her mother! Have you any
idea what *she's* contemplating doing with her share
when she receives it?'

Really wishing she had never begun the conversation
now, Raina shook her head. 'N-no, I haven't,' she
owned reluctantly.

'A string of race horses, no less, would you believe!

Not just one, or perhaps two ... oh, no, Adele aims to make a real splash in the racing world. She wants a string of them! Probably because she sees herself as the glamorous owner accepting winner's trophies before masses of admiring associates,' concluded Faith with a touch of spite.

Raina didn't comment but rashly seized the chance to channel Faith's thoughts towards the topic she usually enjoyed best—herself. 'And you? Do you and Steven have any plans in mind as well?' Never doubting for one moment that they wouldn't have. Faith wasn't exactly a shrinking violet either when it came to creating impressions.

'Oh, yes, we have very definite plans,' her cousin declared in a totally different, self satisfied voice. 'I've seen a house in Vaucluse that's just come on the market. It has a full size tennis court, pool, its own harbourside beach, marina, everything, and I'm determined to have it. Of course its price equals its position, but as I said to Steven, it's important that one keeps up appearances, especially in his profession. A successful lawyer should look successful in all aspects. Besides,' she hunched a green and cream silk-clad shoulder negligently, 'our present house simply isn't large enough any more for the entertaining we do. It has only five bedrooms, and there's just no room for a sauna and spa—both of which the other already has— or even for a terrace to be installed for dancing.' She gave a smooth little laugh. 'I've always envied you that lovely wide terrace of yours that you and your mother use so effectively for parties, you know.'

As well as their riverside mooring, tennis court, and spa, by the sound of it, speculated Raina sardonically. They didn't have a sauna either, and Faith already had a beautiful swimming pool, but her eldest cousin had always hated anyone having something she didn't.

'It sounds very ... imposing,' was her only, tactful acknowledgement, though.

'Oh, it is,' Faith concurred swiftly. 'And I thought, just to complete it, we would buy ourselves matching cars too. BMWs for preference. A lot of our friends are driving those rather than a Mercedes these days.'

Raina smiled, as if in support of the decision, but refrained from answering. Actually, she was becoming a little tired of hearing all the ways her relatives were planning on spending the money that would accrue from the estate, and particularly when the provider of a large percentage of that money had only just been laid to rest! She even tended to think Faith's proposed purchases were no less wastefully extravagant than Adele's and her Aunt Olivia's, because the house Faith and Steven, together with their two children, already occupied had always appeared to her to be somewhat too large for just the four of them, anyway, despite her cousin's assertions to the contrary.

'Of course Malcolm needs the money to pay off his debts,' disclosed Faith, claiming Raina's attention once again. 'At least, that's what I hope he intends to do with it! He borrowed quite heavily from Steven some months back and as far as I can see this is likely to be the only chance Steven has of being repaid.'

'You mean, he's already spent the inheritance he received from your parents?' Raina half gasped, half laughed, although the last she tried hard to camouflage. She knew Malcolm liked to enjoy the good life, but being a wealthy woman in her own right, Bridget Cameron had also left him, as well as his sister, quite a considerable legacy.

'As much as he could get his hands on,' Faith relayed in a contemptuously disapproving tone. 'Fortunately, the capital's still intact, but he's certainly managed to dispose of everything else. It's a pity he doesn't settle down to some decent occupation instead of frittering his life, and his fortune, away in such an irresponsible manner. All he ever does is go to parties, gamble, and get his picture in all the newspapers and magazines!'

Oh, yes, Malcolm was a carefree playboy of the first water, all right, Raina was prepared to concede, but of all her cousins he was still the one she liked best. He was charming, gentlemanly, generous, and extremely popular with both sexes. He was also very well acquainted with everybody who frequented the social scene in every capital city in the country, and who, because of his agreeable disposition, was always a welcome guest at any elite function as a result. Raina also liked him because he had a sense of humour; something she often suspected none of her other relatives possessed.

'He does also provide Steven with introductions to a great many wealthy clients, though, doesn't he?' she couldn't help but point out, ironically, at length. Faith definitely had no complaints about her brother's social connections on those occasions, she recalled.

'For which Steven always sees he is well remunerated!' snapped her cousin touchily.

'Although not because Malcolm has ever expected, or requested such recompense.'

'No—well—that still hasn't stopped him from accepting something in return!' Faith blustered. Then with a composing intake of breath she continued in her more normal autocratic manner, 'Not that Steven has ever *needed* his introductions, anyway. After all, he isn't a Queen's Counsel for nothing. He *is* a very skilful lawyer, as I'm sure even you would have to admit.'

'It was never my intention to infer he wasn't,' returned Raina drily. 'I was merely attempting to show that Malcolm's way of life does have its uses at times.'

'Uses that are far out-weighed by his purposeless

style of living, and gambling excesses! He's nothing more than a lazy, good-for-nothing spendthrift living beyond his means—as evidenced by his having to borrow from Steven—and whose only ambition is the pursuit of his own pleasures!' Faith was determined to have the last word.

This time Raina allowed her to, judging the more she said in Malcolm's defence the worse his sister's criticisms became, and resumed her absent contemplation of the passing countryside instead.

Presently, they turned off the road they had been following, but with the change in direction Raina now found the sun streaming hotly on to her through the open window and thereby reminding her she hadn't yet removed her jacket, as she had been wanting to do all day, but which she now did gratefully. She also discovered herself to be feeling quite drowsy—when all was said and done, ever since early that morning she had covered a great many miles by one form of transport or another—and as her eyelids began to droop she finally gave up trying to keep them open altogether and dozed fitfully for the remainder of the journey.

She was eventually awoken by the vociferous sound of dogs barking mixed with the high-pitched voices of children, and on realising that the station wagon had ceased its bouncing, jolting motion, deduced that they had at last reached their destination and looked about her consideringly as she slowly alighted.

They had halted beside a wide expanse of green lawn that spread out before a white, two-storeyed, lace-balconied building of generous proportions that seemed vaguely familiar to her. To the left a group of bright-eyed and laughing native children clustered about the legs of a tall water tank stand that supported a riotously flowering purple bougainvillaea, the excitement

visible on their faces indicating that the arrival of
visitors, and especially so many new ones, was still
something of a novelty. The dogs, blue heelers for the
most part, and certainly less shy, bounded towards the
two vehicles eagerly until a word of command from
Dev Masters had them retreating to the shade of the
tank stand also.

Returning her attention to the palm and raintree
surrounded homestead, Raina saw a slimly built, brown
haired woman of some forty years step through the
open front door on to the fully flyscreened verandah,
her pleasant face already wearing a welcoming
expression. Dressed neatly but plainly, Raina guessed
her to be the housekeeper, and had her assumption
confirmed a few minutes later after they had all made
their way inside.

'I have afternoon tea ready, but no doubt you would
prefer to freshen up beforehand, so if you'd like to
follow me I'll show you to your rooms first and then I'll
bring the tea out on to the verandah for you,' Ann
Tierney proposed after the introductions had been
completed, and began leading the way up a handsomely
carved staircase. 'One of the men will bring your
luggage to your rooms shortly.'

Along with the others, Raina accepted the suggestion
gratefully and was soon surveying the blue and white
decorated room allocated to her appreciatively. Open,
both in size and by virtue of every window and door
having been pushed wide to let in every possible breath
of stirring air, it was also pleasantly cool due to the
slowly rotating fan overhead, while being at the side of
the house it provided from the balcony a beautiful view
between spreading cassias and pandanus palms down
the high slope on which the homestead was situated to a
gleaming river below, as well as the yellow cane grass
plains with their sprinkling of rotund boabs beyond.

With the delivery of her case, Raina hurriedly removed her skirt and blouse and after washing her face and hands in the compact bathroom that led off her room, changed into a cooler dress she had thankfully thought to bring with her. Then having applied a fresh coating of peach coloured lipstick, she ran a comb through her hair and set off downstairs again.

From those other rooms that she passed, she could see that the rest of the house was furnished as comfortably as her own bedroom, and although most of the furniture wasn't new, it was obviously of a very high quality. But the fact that it was so solid and expensive-looking brought a slight frown to her forehead when she remembered that Davey Newell had said that Dev Masters was only the manager of Ajax Downs. In her estimation, it seemed more suited to an owner's style of living, but then, perhaps those he managed it for liked to visit and stay a while every so often and preferred to relax in the most comfortable surroundings they could provide while doing so, she speculated briefly before stepping out on to the verandah and forgetting the subject altogether on seeing Adele and her two male cousins already seated around a large white, wrought iron table, along with Charley Lawrence and their host.

'Come and sit beside me, angel face,' urged Malcolm with a smile. 'I've hardly had an opportunity to say more than a couple of words to you all day.'

'Thank you, handsome, I think I will,' Raina laughingly answered in kind as she accepted the vacant seat next to him. That it was also the seat furthest away from the station's manager was just an added bonus, she decided pleasurably.

'What would you care to drink, Raina?' Dev enquired in a deeply pleasant voice that had her looking across the table at him in sudden surprise. Not only was it his use of her name that caught her offguard, but the unexpectedly normal tone he had used as well. She supposed because she had anticipated him doing nothing but finding more fault with her. 'Tea ... coffee?' he went on, indicating the two pots already on the table, together with a plate of wafer-thin sandwiches and another of small iced cakes. 'Or maybe you'd like something cool ... or even in this line, perhaps?' This time motioning towards the cans of beer the men had before them.

'No, I think I'd prefer tea, thank you,' she replied coolly. Just because he had deigned to speak decently to her for once—and no doubt solely because there were others present!—he needn't think she was going to fall all over him as her glamorous cousin was evidently doing!

'I'll be mother and pour for you, shall I?' It was Adele herself who spoke now, reaching for the appropriate pot, and somehow making it sound as if the younger girl wasn't capable of doing it for herself.

'If you like,' shrugged Raina indifferently. Adele had always seemed to think that the eight year difference in their ages gave her the right to patronise her youngest cousin.

Beside her, Malcolm flicked open a gold cigarette case. 'And one of these to go with it?' he offered. Adding in a humorously meaningful aside, 'You look as if you could use one.'

That at least brought a lightening to her expression. 'I look that bad?' she half laughed, half grimaced under cover of her aunt and Faith's arrival as she accepted a cigarette from him and nodded her thanks after he had lit it.

'You could never look bad,' he declared fondly. 'However, I do suspect today has meant more to you than you probably expected it would.' He cocked a quizzical brow. 'Am I right?'

Raina drew on her cigarette thoughtfully and then gave a slight hunch with a slender shoulder. 'I'm not sure why it should have done ... but, yes, I think maybe it has somehow.'

'And not only the funeral, hmm?'

'I don't follow you,' she frowned.

'Those birds diverted my attention during the service too, and I saw you looking out over that land. It got to you, didn't it?' he smiled crookedly.

Had it? She remembered thinking something similar when she was on her way to Wallaby Creek, but now, as then, she was strangely reluctant to admit as much. 'I—I certainly find it attractive, if that's what you mean,' she therefore parried.

Malcolm's lips twisted sceptically, as if he could see through her evasion, then he leant a little closer as Olivia and Faith also became seated at the table and began helping themselves to tea. 'Listen, little one,' he urged in a completely serious tone. 'If you want to keep Alliance, then do so. Don't you let them,' nodding faintly towards their other relatives, 'force you into doing something you may regret, just because they're anxious to get their hands on the proceeds. Hayes never gave in to their constant demands for the Estate to be dissolved, so why should you ... if you do want it retained.'

'Except that he happened to be a *male*,' Raina reminded with sardonic emphasis. 'Whereas I'm only a mere female whose vote, as Faith eagerly pointed out on the way here, doesn't really count anyway because the property still has to be run by one of those said males!' She sent him a partly flippant, partly serious glance. 'I don't suppose you'd care for the position, would you?'

'Oh, no, angel face, I'm sorry but you should realise it's no use looking in my direction,' he returned wryly.

'If I'd had any inclinations to stay on the land I had the perfect opportunity to do so when my own father died, but I'm afraid my interests lay elsewhere. There's no reason why you can't do something to solve that particular problem, though.'

'Such as?'

'Marry one of those many escorts I've seen you with from time to time,' he proposed unexpectedly. 'Surely there must be one of them you could see in that role if the matter's important enough to you.'

Raina blinked. Marriage! That was taking it to rather drastic lengths, wasn't it? Besides . . . 'Quite apart from the fact that each of them would undoubtedly be more at home in the stock market rather than a cattle market,' she quipped ironically. 'It's not even as if *I* know anything about running a property, and especially one the size of Alliance.' Three-quarters of a million acres wasn't exactly a little plot you could fumble your way on. 'And if the family suspected the management was being undertaken by an overseer or someone like that, they would very soon have it adjudged as breaking the terms of the Estate, I'm sure.'

'Mmm, you're probably right there,' he owned in rueful accents.

However, the fact that he had at least tried to think of a manner in which to prevent the sale—that was, if she really didn't want it to proceed, she inserted swiftly—had her eyeing him curiously. 'You sound almost as if you don't want the place sold yourself, Malcolm, and yet from something else Faith said, I understood you wouldn't exactly be averse to—umm—receiving some extra funds at the moment.'

'Oh, sure, I certainly wouldn't say no to them if they came my way,' he admitted with a laugh. 'But I'm not completely stony, if that's what you're thinking, and provided you're in the right place at the right time and you know the right people there are always opportunities for making a few thousand here and there. Faith needn't worry, Steven will get his money—I've never welched on a debt yet—but if it's not repaid during the next couple of months, it no doubt will be before the years out.' He paused. 'No, I just figured you might not be quite as enthusiastic about selling now as the rest of them are, and if so, then despite their having arranged between themselves just what was to happen to the Estate before they even arrived here, you shouldn't allow them to compel you into acceding to their wishes, particularly when it was your father's property and, therefore, your birthright, after all. The only thing Alliance ever meant to the rest of them—me included, I guess, if I'm honest—is as a very handy meal ticket . . . nothing else.'

Much as her mother had claimed, Raina recollected pensively. 'If only Clark had lived all of this would probably have been avoided,' she sighed.

'Not necessarily,' Malcolm disagreed with an eloquent shaping of his mouth. 'He may not have been any more enamoured of a grazier's life than the rest of us are.'

A more than distinct possibility if the family as a whole was anything to gauge by, she conceded.

'So what are you two discussing so earnestly? The relief it will be to have things finalised at last?' Adele suddenly enquired brightly, and successfully ending their conversation.

'Isn't that what's on each of our minds?' averred Faith as if it was a foregone conclusion, and saving either Raina or Malcolm the need to answer as a result.

'It certainly is on mine,' chimed in Olivia, helping herself to a cake. 'I never did like living on Alliance, even though I was born there. All that dust and heat, and we wouldn't see anybody from one month to the next. I left when I was seventeen, you know,' she said for Dev's benefit, 'and went to live with my mother's family in Adelaide. Oh, we had some lovely parties there, just about every week, and all the young men came calling . . .' Her voice faded away as she smiled in remembrance. 'Of course, if our homestead had been more like this one,' glancing about her approvingly, 'it might have been different, but it was much smaller than this, and Hayes and Quint never seemed interested in parties and having fun, anyway. All they ever did was work!' The last was somewhat resentfully stated.

The profits from which she had never once objected to, though, grimaced Raina silently, and then pulled herself up short. Come to think of it, neither had she ever objected, and even though her father had been the one to cut her out of *his* life, maybe their cases weren't so dissimilar after all—as someone she preferred not to think about had claimed so succinctly only earlier in the day!

'Never mind, Aunt Olivia.' It was Faith who spoke up bracingly. 'All that will be forgotten once and for all very shortly now, and then . . .'

'I'll be able to buy my plane,' cut in the older woman, brightening considerably. 'Next month even, maybe.'

'Er—I shouldn't rush into anything if I were you, Olivia,' Charley Lawrence now entered the conversation to counsel in gruff tones. 'No matter what's decided with regard to the estate, nothing can be done until probate has been granted on your brother's share of it first, don't forget.'

'Oh!' Olivia's plump little face seemed to crumple. 'No one told me that.' Her china blue eyes held a disappointed and accusing light as they swept over the others at the table.

'Only because no one realised it was necessary,' explained Steven, if a little impatiently. 'After all, we went through exactly the same procedure when both your husband and your other brother died.'

Olivia pinched her lips together like a sulky child. 'I'd forgotten,' she said on an aggrieved note.

Since she had also failed to think of it, Raina could sympathise with her aunt. In any case, after having been raised in a preponderantly male atmosphere where women had apparently only been considered good for having children—preferably male!—and keeping the homestead in order, perhaps it wasn't surprising the poor woman was somewhat on the feather-brained side, she mused astringently. In consequence, she smiled encouragingly at her eldest relative and sought to find another topic to pursue.

'I'll bet you can remember if you've ever been to Ajax Downs before, though,' she asserted, picking on a subject her aunt quite possibly knew something about. 'When you used to live in the north, I mean. I know there seemed to be something vaguely familiar about it to me when we arrived.'

Her aunt frowned for a moment and then nodded, looking much happier. 'Yes, now that you mention it, I do believe I have been here previously. A couple of times, in fact. Only then it was owned by a family called . . . called Tarrant. Yes, that's it, Tarrant!' she repeated triumphantly.

'Your memory's certainly good for names, Mrs Hewitt,' applauded Dev pleasantly. 'That's the family the Territory Pastoral Company bought the property from eight years ago, all right. While as for it also seeming familiar to your niece,' he continued with a briefly speculative look in Raina's direction, 'that's probably because she was once something of a regular visitor here, I've been told. Apparently the Tarrants also had a young daughter and Raina's mother would often bring her over with her when she was feeling the need for company.'

Olivia nodded knowingly. 'Mmm, Eve could never take the isolation either. She much preferred a more socially involved life, the same as I did.'

Something Raina knew well had been a strong contributing factor to the break-up of her parents' marriage, although she was a little surprised to learn that she had also been a regular visitor to Ajax Downs as a result, for only the homestead had struck a receptive chord in her memory. She could remember nothing of the people who had once lived there. Before she could mention as much, however, Adele sought clarification for what obviously was uppermost in her own mind.

'You said a pastoral company bought the property?' she queried of Dev. 'Does that mean you've since purchased it, or—or are you simply managing it for them?' In a noticeably disappointed voice.

Either oblivious to, or unperturbed by her tone, he shrugged equably. 'Just managing it,' he drawled.

'I see,' she acknowledged, now also looking as crestfallen as she had previously sounded, and causing her youngest cousin to wonder sardonically if perhaps she now considered Dev Masters wasn't quite her kind of man, as she had first proclaimed, after all.

'The Territory part of the title being due to the company originating in the Northern Territory, I presume,' surmised Steven, more interested in the business side of the subject.

'That's right,' came the nodded confirmation. 'It's a privately owned company consisting of some four properties in all. The other three being in the Territory.'

'Hmm, I thought I hadn't heard of them before,' pondered Steven in his most judicious manner. 'But an expanding one, I gather, since they've now moved into W.A. as well.'

There was a quick flash of strong white teeth as Dev

smiled. 'It has its moments,' he conceded, though somewhat non-committally to Raina's mind.

'And just how big is Ajax Downs? Larger than Alliance?' inserted Faith. Size appeared to be of prime importance to her at the moment.

'About a quarter as large again,' she was informed impassively. 'It's roughly a million acres. Much the same as most properties in the Kimberley today.'

Faith seemed suitably impressed, if a little put out by the knowledge that Alliance was smaller. 'You must have an even greater wages bill than Alliance does, then.' The number of men employed on the family property had also always been a bone of contention between Hayes Cameron and the city based family shareholders.

'I couldn't really say, although I shouldn't imagine so. These days we mainly muster by helicopter which, although expensive during the time they're in action, does at least mean that over the years we've been able to reduce our ground staff in order to offset the cost.' Pausing, his firmly moulded mouth took on an oblique slant. 'Hayes, with his love of horses, however, preferred to retain the old methods ... as have a number of others in the region.'

'Old, backward ways!' decried Faith promptly, exasperatedly.

'Not necessarily,' contradicted Dev with a shake of his head. 'As it happens, on a lot of stations where they've been mustering by air for a number of years they're now finding it becoming less effective and they're having to return to using more stockmen again because the cattle now realise that the choppers can't hurt them and so they're beginning to ignore them. It's one of those cases of familiarity breeding contempt, I guess.'

'Although you haven't experienced any such problem as yet?'

'No, not to date, I must admit.'

'And neither would they on Alliance since the cattle there aren't accustomed to being mustered by air!' Faith asserted in victorious tones. 'That at least means we can cut some costs to a minimum immediately.'

'But I thought we had agreed the whole estate was to be sold,' put in her aunt, looking bewildered.

'Well, of course it is,' conceded Faith, returning the older woman's glance irritably. 'But in the meantime, I see no reason why we should pay out so much in wages when it's evidently quite unnecessary. We may as well make the most profit we can, and firing at least half the staff as soon as possible would seem to me to be a good step in that direction. I mean, we don't need to wait until probate's been granted in order to save ourselves some money, do we, Charley?'

Obviously startled by having been suddenly brought into the conversation, Charley looked a little uncomfortable for a moment or two. 'Well ... no,' he finally confessed, but with patent reluctance.

Not that Faith paid any mind to that. 'Then it's agreed that's what will be done?' She sent a sweeping, confident gaze around the table.

With two exceptions, there were immediate comments of approval from the family shareholders.

'Sorry, but you can count me out,' Malcolm vetoed calmly. 'The scheme is completely unwarranted as far as I'm concerned.'

'While I—to put it bluntly—think it absolutely stinks!' flared Raina, not mincing her words. 'I was speaking to some of those men today that you're so casually, and callously, intending sacking, and the idea of repaying their loyalty to my father in such a manner—and all for a few extra dollars not one of you really needs,' her blue eyes denounced them contemptuously, 'I find totally obnoxious, not to mention just plain grasping!'

Of all of them, only her aunt began to look somewhat abashed. Steven seemed to be speaking for the others when he began to remonstrate, 'I wouldn't exactly call it a *few* dollars, Raina! By the time the Estate is finally settled it will be a great deal more than that, you can take my word for it!'

'Besides which it would be far better for all concerned if, instead of restoring to emotional judgments, you paid more attention to the cold hard facts and allowed yourself to be guided by those who know better than you on the matter!' added Adele censuringly.

'Except that, in this instance—cold hard facts, or otherwise—I think I would rather be guided by my *own* knowledge, thanks all the same!' Raina retorted defiantly. 'I want none of it . . . and that's final!'

'Hear, hear!' endorsed Malcolm, drawing their attention to himself now.

'Oh, yes, I might have known you would agree with her! They say a fool and his money are soon parted, and you've certainly never been able to handle your assets competently, have you, Malcolm?' his sister sniped. 'Well, the next time you run short, let's hope you approach Raina for a loan instead of Steven and myself!'

Not looking the slightest bit disturbed by her disclosure, Malcolm tut-tutted chidingly. 'Washing the family's dirty linen in public, Faith?' he mocked. 'I'm sure it's of no interest whatsoever to Dev and Charley.'

His sister at least had the grace to appear somewhat discomfited, although it was her aunt who exclaimed distractedly, 'No! No, of course not. P-perhaps we could leave the matter until after dinner, or—or even some other time.' Olivia was a great one for putting off anything that was likely to be at all unpleasant.

'Meanwhile . . .,' interposed Dev smoothly, beginning to rise to his feet as from behind the homestead came the sound of nearing horses, of the dogs starting to bark again, and of men's voices. 'I'll have to ask you to excuse me, I'm afraid. There are a few things I still need to attend to before dark.' Pushing in his chair, he retrieved his wide brimmed hat that had been sharing a hook in one of the verandah posts with a hanging basket of ferns and settled it firmly on his head. 'Dinner is at seven, although we usually gather in the billiard room for a drink or two beforehand, so if you would care to join us I'll see you again then.' And with a polite tug on the brim of his hat he began walking away along the verandah.

Raina watched in absent contemplation his tall, now drill-covered form depart, speculating as to whether he really did have work to do, or whether that had merely been an excuse to escape their family wrangling. Not that she would altogether blame him if it had been the latter—she also found the continual bickering, that occurred whenever they all got together, tiresome most times too—but conversely, or perversely, the suspicion that he couldn't find anything commendable about them, as displayed by his original depreciating comments regarding herself, gave rise to an uncontrollable feeling of smouldering indignation.

Just because he had seen fit to offer them accommodation at Ajax Downs—which, strictly speaking, wasn't even his place to do since he only managed the property on someone else's behalf, anyway!—it certainly didn't give him the right to make such arbitrary, not to say arrogant, judgments on either herself or any other members of her family, nor even their chosen lifestyles!

'Then as Charley will be reading Hayes's will after dinner, I suggest we discuss this matter of reduced staff levels further then in private,' Steven interrupted Raina's rather resentful musings in a decisive tone that was apparently designed to overcome any opposition.

Already in a nettled mood because of one male, Raina wasn't now about to meekly accept attempted domination by another, however. As her tenacious resistance showed. 'Since I have no intention of changing my mind, there doesn't seem much point,' she defied. 'All such decisions do still require a *unanimous* vote, don't they, Charley?' She looked to the estate's solicitor for support.

From the other end of the table, he nodded resolutely. 'Oh, yes!' his confirmation was no less irrefutably stated.

'Which is utterly absurd!' seethed Adele. 'And precisely the reason why I've always claimed it would be much more rational, and fair, if all decisions were those of the majority! This way, it's always the *minority* who have control!'

Charley shrugged dispassionately. Over the years he had become used to such complaints, among numerous others, from non-contributory share-holders. 'It's merely a condition to ensure that whatever decisions are made have the approval of all. Nevertheless, for those who are dissatisfied with the manner in which the Estate is controlled, there is always the provision that permits them to sell their shares to another shareholder,' he reminded pointedly.

'What! Sell out now, on the eve of what we've all been waiting for ... the final, largest payout?' she scoffed. 'That's the most ridiculous suggestion I've ever heard!'

'Then it would appear that you will just have to content yourself with that considerable settlement, wouldn't it?' he proposed in softly subtle tones.

'Put that way, yes, I suppose it does! Thanks to

Malcolm and Raina!' heaved Faith with patent displeasure as she re-entered the conversation. Gaining her feet, she directed her glaring gaze solely towards the younger girl. 'Although this evening's decision concerning the estate in general had certainly better be another matter!' With which last scarcely veiled threat she swept from the verandah into the house.

No sooner had she departed than an obviously bashful, but smiling house girl came to collect the tea trays and, in a mixture of moods Raina and the others thoughtfully began to make their way inside the homestead too in order to prepare for dinner and the evening ahead.

CHAPTER THREE

ALTHOUGH dressed and ready by six-fifteen, instead of heading for the billiard room straight away, Raina chose to take a walk around the upstairs balcony. The light was fading quickly—as it always did in the tropics—but on reaching the rear of the building there was still sufficient left for her to be able to see reasonably clearly.

To the right of the homestead she could make out what seemed to be a well-tended and surprisingly assorted vegetable garden, while just beyond it flourished a variety of fruit trees; mangoes, bananas, citrus, pawpaws, avocados, and beside them a trellis supporting a luxuriant passionfruit vine.

The view in the opposite direction mainly contained an array of out-buildings; a couple of small cottages, staff quarters for both married and single men, workshops, garages, machinery and storage sheds. Beyond, there was a set of strongly constructed cattle yards complete with loading ramps, a fowl-house with its attendant yard wherein a host of black hens were presently being fed, plus a large, and at the moment well-utilised, horse paddock.

The scene succeeded in reviving even more memories for Raina—except that as she recalled it, Alliance hadn't been on quite such a grand scale—and with them came the unexpected but overwhelming desire to see her father's property again as soon as possible. In fact, she would go over there tomorrow if it could be arranged, she decided impulsively as she turned away from the balcony. She *had* promised Daniel she would visit the station, and since she didn't envisage being at Ajax Downs for very long there was no time like the present.

Downstairs once more, Raina experienced no difficulty in locating the billiard room due to the voices that could be heard emanating therefrom, and simply allowed her ears to guide her. On stepping through the doorway her first impression was that it was an extremely large room, as well as a very masculine one with its scattering of heavy leather armchairs, the gigantic pair of mounted buffalo horns on one wall that immediately captured one's attention, a rack of both large and small bore rifles decorating another, and by no means least, the solid billiard table that dominated the room.

She also noted in that first glance that her female relatives had elected to really dress for dinner in the strictest sense of the word, whereas the men, including Dev Masters and another two she hadn't seen before, had opted for something less grandiose, as she had.

'Hi! I'm Bevan Rawson, the jackaroo—third year, of course—round here.' The youngest, and closest, of the two strangers came forward immediately to greet her with a smile on seeing her enter the room. Only a little older than her own twenty-two years, with mid-brown hair and hazel eyes, and dressed in dark pants with a check, short sleeved shirt open at the throat, he looked cheerful and friendly, and completely at ease in his surroundings. 'And since you're the only one of our visitors I haven't met as yet, you must be Raina Cameron. Right?' His head tilted enquiringly.

'Right,' smiled Raina in return. 'I'm pleased to meet you, Bevan.'

'The same here,' he nodded, his eyes taking in her delicately formed features pleasurably. 'So what can I get you to drink, Raina? Whisky, gin, sherry?'

Indicating the dark red wood bar set beneath the mounted buffalo horns where an extensive assortment of tall jugs, glasses, and bottles was visible. 'Just name your poison and I'll fetch it for you.'

'Oh, sherry, I think, thanks,' she advised, deciding on something safe. After the way in which Faith and Adele had been talking during the afternoon she suspected she could well need to have all her wits about her for this evening.

With his departure, Raina suddenly found Dev at her side. Since he had been in conversation with her aunt and Adele when she entered, she hadn't realised he'd even noticed her arrival. Tonight he was wearing dark pants much the same as Bevan's, except that his were of a considerably more expensive material, and his broader shoulders were covered by a silk knit shirt that only seemed to emphasise their width and the muscularity of his chest. It made her aware of a heavily masculine aura about him that she found oddly disturbing.

'You'd better come and meet Joe,' he invited impassively, taking hold of her arm and steering her towards the older man who was talking to Steven and Malcolm. 'I see Bevan's already introduced himself and is attending to a drink for you.'

Raina nodded, and trying to ignore the even stranger effect his touch on her arm appeared to be having on her, allowed herself to be led down the room.

At their approach, all three men turned to face them, their expressions varying. Malcolm's was plainly welcoming, Steven's a trifle stand-offish—as a result of her refusing to agree to the scheme that had been put forward earlier, she supposed—the other man's politely expectant, but still somewhat cool at the same time. He doesn't approve of me, Raina abruptly deduced in surprise. But why? To her knowledge she hadn't ever met him before, so what could she possibly have done to put that hard look in his brown eyes?

'Joe Tierney, Raina Cameron,' introduce Dev concisely. 'Joe—Ann's husband—is the overseer here.'

Raina smiled brightly, hoping to overcome some of the older man's obvious resistance. 'How do you do?'

'Miss Raina,' he acknowledged stolidly with a brief nod.

'Please, just Raina,' she urged, making another attempt, and then gave an inward sigh on merely receiving another brief nod in response. She decided to give it one last try. 'And—er—have you worked on Ajax Downs for long, Joe?'

'More than ten years. It's a good property.'

At least that was an improvement. 'So you didn't come with Dev, then?'

'No,' was the sparse reply, and although she waited for him to continue, nothing else was forthcoming, and she was forced to concede that she was wasting her time. Perhaps he was simply a not untypical taciturn bushman, she reflected. Not that that was really a satisfactory explanation for his coolness, of course, but what other reason could there be?

'Your drink.' Bevan now returned, holding out a glass towards her which she accepted from him gratefully. She was beginning to feel in need of one! 'Sorry I took so long but I had to open a new bottle. I also took a guess as to your preference and selected sweet. I hope that's okay.'

'Yes, fine,' she averred, taking a sip. Actually, she preferred dry, but was too thankful for his more open, and certainly less dour presence to care at the moment.

Unaware of the tension that had been building, at least as far as Raina was concerned, he continued in the same affable vein. 'You're planning to stay for a few days, I trust. We don't often get this many visitors, and especially not such attractive ones.'

Beside her, Raina sensed rather than saw Dev's hard look in his jackaroo's direction, and made her expression doubly appreciative as a result. 'No, we're only staying overnight, I believe. I wasn't there when the arrangements were made. Nevertheless, I am hoping to visit Alliance tomorrow if possible on my way back to Wallaby Creek.'

'You do intend to actually set foot on the place, then?' came the sardonic sounding query from Dev.

'Since I promised Daniel I would, yes,' she glanced up to retort swiftly, although that didn't stop a rosy flush of selfconscious colour from staining her cheeks on remembering that she'd had no such plan in mind when she'd arrived. 'Perhaps you have some suggestion as to how I might best reach the property?' She lifted a challenging brow.

'From here, by car, I guess,' he shrugged with negligent grace. 'Or I could always fly you there if you've found the roads too much for you, and you're also in a hurry to return to the city.' Again that mocking edge crept into his voice.

In response, Raina's chin rose to a higher level. 'No, I've no objection to travelling by road. Provided it doesn't inconvenience you at all, of course.' Her own tone wasn't entirely free from sarcasm now either.

'No sweat, it won't.' His reply was nothing if not unequivocal. Then suddenly one corner of his shapely mouth sloped upwards. 'Although maybe it will you.'

'In what way?'

'Because it means that, unless you're only planning a hello/goodbye flying visit, you won't reach Wallaby Creek in time to pick up a charter flight going across to Derby.'

'Then I shall just have to wait in town until I can get

one, shan't I?' Did he honestly think she was *that* anxious to return home?

'At that hotel?' cut in Steven with a scornful half laugh. 'I wouldn't advise it! It's no five star establishment, you know, and one night there was more than enough for me. It was as rowdy as hell and filled with the toughest looking characters I think I've ever seen!'

'They don't call the area "the last frontier" for nothing,' grinned Bevan with evident amusement at Steven's disdainful countenance. 'This country is still being pioneered, and that calls for tough men. If they weren't, they wouldn't survive.'

He might just as well not have spoken for all the effect it had on Steven. 'That's neither here nor there,' he contended on a pompous note. 'I still say it's no place for my cousin to be considering staying on her own. In fact . . .,' he expelled a long-suffering breath as he directed his gaze towards Raina, 'I can't even see why you should wish to visit Alliance in the first place. It's not as if the place can have any meaning for you. After all, you were only a child when you saw it last. I think you'd do better to forget the whole silly idea altogether and fly back to Darwin with us tomorrow instead in the plane we've arranged to pick us up here. Then if you do have to stay overnight you can at least book into a decent hotel.'

'Oh, I think Raina would find the Wallaby Creek Hotel decent enough,' inserted Dev evenly, much to Raina's surprise, and before she could grasp the opportunity to tell her cousin what she thought of his remarks concerning her visiting Alliance. 'Granted, for the most part it may have a less—umm—refined clientele than those you usually patronise, but I very much doubt she would come to any harm for all that. Up here, tough looking or not, men still believe it's

their responsibility to protect women, not attack them
. . . as we so often read occurs in your more cultured
and sophisticated cities.'

Just what Steven would have said to that rather
sardonically worded remark was never discovered,
because just then Ann Tierney came in to advise that
dinner was about to be served and the moment passed
as they finished their drinks and all made their way
across the passage to the dining room. Which was
perhaps as well, mused Raina wryly, if the sharpening
look that had came over Steven's face was any
indication.

The dining room turned out to be not quite so large
as the billiard room, but still certainly spacious enough
to accommodate them all at the long, polished
rosewood table with ease. Dev sat at the head of the
table with Olivia on his right and Raina on his left. In
deference to the fact that it was her father who had
died, she supposed. Ann Tierney occupied the seat at
the other end of the table with her husband on one side
and Bevan on the other, the remaining visitors being
seated between.

To her relief, Raina found Charley Lawrence to have
been seated on her left—if it had been any of her
relatives except Malcolm, she was positive she would
only have been subjected throughout the meal to a
string of criticisms for her stand of the afternoon—and
knowing her aunt would keep Dev occupied with a
steady flow of idle chatter, felt free to devote her
attention to the older man. She liked Charley. The more
so as he had been the family's only source of
information regarding Alliance for some time now.

In a way he had come to represent something of a
father-figure to her, because on many occasions when
she had been younger it had been to him she had turned
for advice as to how she should cast her vote in matters

relating to the estate rather than to her stepfather, Michael. It wasn't that she had considered Michael incapable of advising her. After all, he was a very successful businessman himself. It was just that ever since she turned eighteen and became able to vote in her own right, until then her father had retained her proxy in accordance with the estate's terms, for some strange reason she had wanted on more than one occasion to vote as her father would have wished—a probably unrealistic and unappreciated gesture, she admitted— and Charley had been the only one who could have informed her of that with any degree of certainty.

'Well, it seems the rest of them are finally going to achieve their desires, doesn't it?' she commented reflectively soon after they began eating.

'You're not going to vote against a sale?' he enquired, his glance watchful.

'I must confess I wasn't intending to when I left home this morning, but then ...' Pausing, she executed a helpless shrug. 'Without a male vote to support me it has no bearing on whether I do or not now, so I guess I may as well do as they all wish.'

'But then ...?' he picked up subtley.

'Oh, I don't know.' She gave her head a confused shake. 'After seeing the country again I just felt ...' She halted again, not really knowing or able to express exactly what she had felt. 'Well, it seems a pity somehow to think of all those years of effort that have gone into building up the estate simply being ignored because they're more interested in frivolous spending sprees. And all because of that damned clause insisting a male run the estate!' Her voice became caustically charged.

Charley eyed her understandingly. 'Yes, well, I suppose they figured the males in the family were more likely to want to remain on the land, as well as ensure the properties stayed with the family, of course. I guess they just never visualised a whole generation wanting to depart from tradition, which thereby makes Hayes's premature death even more of a tragedy. The hope that maybe at least one of the next generation would feel differently about it was perhaps his strongest reason for holding out against the rest of them so determinedly.'

'Then I'm surprised he didn't marry again himself in order to produce more males who may have followed in his footsteps,' Raina declared in the same slightly acid tones.

'Mainly, I suspect, because his first venture into marriage didn't leave him with a particularly favourable view of the institution,' he revealed in a somewhat whimsical fashion. 'In any case, for a while he and your uncle Quint believed Malcolm was going to be the one to carry on the Estate. At the time he appeared to have a liking for the life, but as you know, after experiencing a taste of city society on leaving school, that was the end of wanting to return to the bush as far as Malcolm was concerned.'

Raina's mouth shaped expressively in acknowledgment, but her thoughts were on the first part of his explanation. 'I don't know why my father wouldn't have had a favourable impression of marriage,' she retorted with some heat. 'He got all he ever wanted out of it, even if poor little Clark was killed. It was Mum it was rough on!'

'Was it?'

For a moment she looked taken aback, and then she maintained, 'But you know it was! She was the stranger to the heat, the dust, the isolation—the last being total during the wet season! She was also the one left on her own for days, sometimes weeks on end while my father was out mustering, and because of that also having to rear her children as good as singlehanded!'

'All of which she was warned about before they were married!'

'Not according to her!'

Picking up the wine glass before him that had been filled earlier, Charley took a slow mouthful. 'Well, she was, I can assure you,' she was informed on an adamant note. 'Although there seems little to be gained in discussing the rights and wrongs of the matter at this late stage.' He hesitated, and then continued resolutely. 'However, there is one thing I think you should know. Despite Eve apparently now claiming otherwise, for your information there never were any hassles about her having sole charge of the children because she made it plain from the day you were born that she *wanted* it that way.'

On the verge of, if not disputing the surprising assertion, then at least questioning it, Raina abruptly did neither. Now that she came to think of it, she couldn't really remember Michael having much say regarding her half-brother's upbringing either. It had always been what her mother thought best for Glen that had held sway, although it wasn't until now that she'd realised as much. She had simply accepted it as a matter of course because her stepfather had never made any objections.

'I'm sorry, I didn't mean to upset you, especially today of all days,' Charley broke in on her reverie apologetically. 'I wasn't attempting to cast aspersions on Eve either. She was always a good mother.'

Raina shook her head, dispelling his worries with a smile. 'No, it's all right. You didn't upset me. You just made me think, that's all.' She shrugged philosophically. 'I guess we can all tend to colour the truth to suit ourselves at times, can't we?'

He nodded gravely, and for a time they both concentrated on their meals.

Looking up again presently to smile at the house girl who had taken away her plate and was now replacing it with a rich creme caramel dessert, Raina's gaze suddenly connected with Dev's.

'You're sure you still want to make that trip tomorrow?' he asked blandly, but with a taunting light in the depths of his dark eyes that was at variance with his voice.

'Of course!' she affirmed unreservedly. And in return for that look rounded her own eyes mockingly. 'Why, are you now regretting having offered?'

'Not at all,' he half smiled, and she was struck by the unexpectedly beguiling quality in the oblique curving of his frankly sensuous mouth. 'I just thought you may have reconsidered but were loath to say so.'

'Well, I haven't,' she all but snapped, annoyed with herself for having found anything about him attractive, as much as with him. 'In fact, I've been thinking I might even stay at Alliance for a day or two until I can get a flight back to Derby instead of waiting at the Creek.' A spur of the moment decision that. Like, right then and there, to be exact! 'That at least should make you happy.'

'I'm not sure why.'

'Well, you won't then have to suffer my obviously distasteful company all the way in to town then, will you?' she gibed.

His eyes ranged over her in a boldly assessing sweep that, to her surprise, had her cheeks going hot with embarrassment. It was a long time since a mere look from a man had been capable of doing that. Usually she managed to remain completely undisturbed.

'Oh, it's not your company I find distasteful, sweetheart,' he drawled explicitly. 'Just your habit of always taking . . . without ever feeling obliged to *give* something in return.'

So he was back to calling her a parasite, was he? she fumed. 'Then if it's so important to you, please allow me to *give* you something in payment for your driving me to Alliance tomorrow,' she proposed with barbed flippancy. 'How much is your time and effort worth? Fifty, a hundred, two hundred dollars? Just put a price on it and I'll be glad to pay it.'

Her hand that had been resting on the table was suddenly gripped by bruising fingers. 'Don't get smart with me, Raina!' Dev ground out in a dangerously low voice between tight lips. 'Not that I should be altogether surprised, I guess. You've probably become so used to buying whatever you want—with the profits from somebody else's labour, of course—that you now think the paying over of money *is* giving!'

'That's not true!' she heaved resentfully, but mindful to keep her voice down. 'Nor do you know the first thing about me! And—and I thought you said men didn't attack women up here!' Glaring meaningfully at the hand still gripping hers in an attempt to put him on the defensive instead.

His eyes gleamed with impenitent laughter. 'Perhaps I should have added . . . unless they're provoked into doing so.'

'And perhaps you don't qualify for inclusion with those "men" either! That being the shortened form for *gentlemen*!' she shot back.

Now the gleam in his thickly framed eyes was joined by a warmly deep laugh issuing from his bronzed throat as he finally saw fit to release her. 'A point to remember, maybe?' He raised a dark brow tauntingly.

'Since I doubt I'll be seeing you again after tomorrow, thankfully I won't need to,' Raina retaliated with acid sweetness. But at the same time very much aware that he had just confirmed her first impression of him. He *was* a man to be reckoned with! Deliberately dismissing, she returned her attention to her dessert.

As soon as the meal was concluded, Raina and her relatives, together with Charley, adjourned to a comfortably furnished sitting room for coffee and the reading of Hayes Cameron's Will. Bevan and Joe returned to the billiard room with theirs, but when Dev would have followed them Charley stopped him.

'Seeing you're mentioned in here too,' he advised, indicating the neatly typewritten sheets he was removing from his brief case, 'I think you're entitled to stay.' A scanning gaze was directed towards the others seated at various points around the room for endorsement.

Although the information caused a few raised brows, their nodded consent was readily given and Dev took a seat near the open doors that gave on to the verandah as Charley began to speak.

In the main Hayes's disposal of his personal estate was much as expected. There were generous legacies for Daniel and Ngarla which also included a few items of a personal nature, plus another couple to stockmen who had served on the property for many years. There were also others of varying amounts to long-supported charities, and a minimal one for his sister, Olivia. Apparently that had been considered obligatory, but just as evidently he hadn't considered anything of the sort was owed to his nieces and nephews for their names were conspicuously absent. A circumstance that created a good deal of indignant and displeased shufflings and murmurings on their part. The remainder was bequeathed to Raina . . . except for the stock horses and working dogs that Hayes had owned personally, and they had been most specifically left to Dev.

As it happened, this bequest caused the greatest outburst of all. Not because any of them were particularly averse to Dev receiving the animals, but because of the nature of the very precise words that had advised them of the fact, for Hayes had openly declared that, 'as I can't trust any of my lazy, good-for-nothing, money-grubbing relatives to see beyond their worth as a realised asset in their anxiety to extract every last cent possible from the undoubted sale of Alliance Station, then I give and bequeath all those horses and dogs that are personally owned by me to my good and trusted friend Devlin Masters, Grazier, of Ajax Downs Station, Shire of Wyndham-East Kimberley, in the State of Western Australia, knowing he will care for and appreciate them as they deserve.'

'Oh dear, oh dear!' fluttered Olivia breathlessly. 'To think my own brother could be so unkind.'

'Lazy! Good-for-nothing!' Faith expostulated in outrage. 'Didn't he realise just how hard Steven and I have worked to attain our present position in society?' Corroborated by her husband's vehement nod.

'And how dare he call us money-grubbing!' Adele displayed her own affront in somewhat more shrill tones. 'We're entitled to whatever profits the Estate made! We're shareholders the same as he was!'

The calmest of them all, Malcolm, lit a cigarette and eyed her with ironical humour. 'Except that I rather think our uncle was of the opinion that those who contributed nothing to the Estate should really receive precisely the same in return.'

Adele glared at him irefully. 'Well, you certainly haven't contributed anything so I fail to see why you're sitting there looking so smug and unaffected! He was referring to you too, you know!' She took a deep breath, regaining some of her composure. 'In any event, those were the terms of the Estate and it's just bad luck if he didn't happen to like them!'

'So it would seem. Although he did at least manage

to have the last word with regard to his private estate, didn't he?' Malcolm's lips twitched expressively.

With a disdainful snort, Adele turned her back on him and continued to vent her aggravation on Faith and Steven's more receptive ears.

Only three of those present didn't make any comment at all. Dev, because the remarks obviously hadn't concerned him, and who was watching the following proceedings through scornful eyes. Charley, who had witnessed many such ructions on previous occasions when dealing with the family shareholders, and was occupying himself with other papers in his brief case while he waited for the tumult to die down. And Raina, who remained quietly in her chair with her head slightly bowed and her even white teeth worrying at her lower lip.

Disappointment and sadness were the emotions she was experiencing, knowing that not even she had been considered sufficiently trustworthy to take responsibility for her father's animals, not to mention having also obviously been included in that lazy, good-for-nothing, money-grubbing category. She smiled wistfully. So much for taking exception to Dev's similar condemnation. Apparently her own father had thought of her in exactly the same uncomplimentary fashion.

Gradually the complaints being voiced by the others were reduced to the occasional muted rumbling, but not to be deprived of her prime reason for having made the long journey, Faith now determinedly called their attention to it.

'Well, now that that's been disposed of—trust Hayes to have been insulting to the last!' she couldn't resist adding acrimoniously, 'perhaps we can get down to the real business of the evening . . . and the principal reason we're all here, I'm sure. To provide Charley with our instructions for the disposal of the Estate in its entirety!'

'And about time too!' lauded Adele without hesitation.

'Right then, since we're all in accord, maybe I should take over from here,' proposed Steven officiously, rising to his feet and pacing about the room in a manner that suggested he saw himself parading in court. 'Since the law is my profession, I can explain in the correct terms just how we wish Charley to word our decision so there can be no disputing our intentions.'

'Oh, what a good idea!' Olivia pressed her hands to her pearl bedecked bosom in relief. 'I was so afraid I wouldn't do it right if we each had to make our own requests.'

Steven half smiled at her patronisingly. 'Don't worry, Olivia, when I'm finished all you'll have to do is sign on the dotted line and our decision to sell will be irrevocable.'

The sound of Charley clearing his throat portentously suddenly had all eyes swinging in his direction. 'Er—you appear to have overlooked something, Steven,' he put forward drily. 'You haven't yet taken a vote to ascertain whether everyone *is* in agreement.'

'But of course we all are!' came the rather impatient assertion. 'Why else would we be here otherwise?'

'To pay your respects to the man who actually made your shareholdings so worthwhile over the years?' Charley's white brows peaked graphically.

'I—well—yes, that too, naturally,' Steven blustered, for once losing some of his pomposity on realising his mistake. 'What I—I really meant, of course, was that was the reason we're all gathered here tonight.'

'And we all know what the result of any vote would be . . . unanimous in favour of selling!' Adele interjected on a confident, though somewhat bored note. 'So why the necessity for having one? Let's just get on with what we're really interested in doing!'

'No, Charley's right.' Steven held up an arresting hand even as he gave the solicitor an acknowledging, if less than genuine smile. 'Everything must be done by the book if it's to be legal and binding. So a show of hands, please, from all those in favour of the disposal of the Cameron Estate.'

Despite still pondering over the events of the day— her father's funeral, Daniel's visible disappointment at the thought of Alliance being sold, her relatives' plans for spending the proceeds when it was, the animals her father hadn't trusted to be left on the property, her own inexplicable feelings on returning to the area, and last but by no means least both Dev and her parent's views regarding herself—Raina was aware that the others, including Malcolm, had immediately raised their hands in response to Steven's request, but with an abrupt, impetuous resolve she steadfastly kept her own at her sides.

'*Raina!*' Faith promptly grated in a menacing tone.

'I'm sorry, but I'm just not sure at the moment,' she defied unflinchingly.

Her cousin's eyes narrowed hostilely and then she turned to Charley. 'Well, her vote isn't absolutely essential, anyway, is it? Not without a male in the family being willing to run the properties.'

After a quick, regretful glance in Raina's direction, Charley shook his head and sighed. 'Under such circumstances . . . no, I'm afraid not,' he admitted with obvious reluctance. 'Nevertheless, if Raina chooses to remain of the same mind, it will of course make it somewhat more difficult, as well as take longer, to have your majority decision sanctioned.'

'You mean, it will be even more months before I can buy my plane?' Olivia fretted, casting her china blue eyes reproachfully in her youngest niece's direction.

'Exactly!' bit out Faith in enraged accents.

'It's simply a dog-in-the-manger attitude when there's no way it can prevent the sale in the long run!' denounced Steven.

'It's also her right to vote as she wishes,' Malcolm defended, and received a faint smile of gratitude from Raina in return.

'Her right!' disputed Adele bitterly. 'And what about ours? Or doesn't she figure they count now that she's received such a tidy sum from her father's estate while of the rest of us got nothing!' She swung to face Raina. 'We're still shareholders, you know, Raina! Even if your father did do his best to make it appear otherwise!'

'I'm well aware that you are, Adele,' the younger girl answered coolly as she rose to her feet. 'However, as Malcolm so correctly said, and whether you like it or not, I do have the right to vote as I think fit—not necessarily as *you* would have me vote—and for as long as the estate remains in force I intend to continue to exercise that right! And now I think it's time for me to say goodnight.' With a defiant angling of her head she about-faced and made her way out of the room before another word could be said.

It had seemed the only course to take when, if she had stayed, she knew without a doubt that she would only have had to suffer more of their attacks, which in turn would only have served to prolong their wrath.

CHAPTER FOUR

NOT unexpectedly, what conversation Raina did have with her relatives the following morning was somewhat strained, except for those times when she spoke to Malcolm, who seemed rather more amused than annoyed with developments. Consequently, she was quite relieved when, after having seen Charley depart by car for Kununurra shortly after breakfast, their chartered plane arrived almost immediately to transport them back to Darwin, from where they would catch afternoon flights to their respective home bases.

Naturally enough, though, Faith wasn't able to depart without adding at least one threatening directive that it would be best if Raina altered her decision very quickly, while Adele, after a last wistfully contemplative look at Dev, had boarded the plane with a resigned shrug that had brought an ironic curve to her cousin's lips. The discovery that their host wasn't the actual owner of Ajax Downs had decreased the glamorous girl's interest markedly, although it was just as apparent that Adele wished it had been otherwise.

'If you're ready, I suggest we start making a move soon too,' Dev turned to Raina to propose once the plane carrying her relatives had disappeared from sight in the azure blue sky. 'It'll take us a good four hours to get there, I expect.'

Raina nodded stiffly. Undoubtedly he was as anxious to see the last of her as she was of him. 'I'll just collect my case—it's already packed—and say goodbye to Ann.'

'Don't worry about your luggage. I'll get that for

you,' he instructed rather than offered as they walked the hundred yards or so from the airstrip back to the homestead.

'Thank you.' She still felt obliged to show some appreciation. 'I'll meet you out the front of the house, shall I?'

He gave a brief shake of his head. 'No, down at the garage, seeing we leave in that direction. It's the second building you'll come to down the back.'

'I'll find it,' she acknowledged as they entered the house and she made to turn in the direction of the kitchen. 'I won't be long.'

Dev didn't even reply, but merely executed a half hearted nod before continuing along the passage towards the stairs, and Raina expelled a dismal breath as she watched him.

At the dinner table last night he had been disconcertingly goading, but now he appeared to have returned to his former attitude of barely concealed dislike. Not that she cared either way, of course, she told herself bracingly, because his opinions were of no concern to her at all. Not at all! she repeated decisively, and cast the matter from her mind as she entered the kitchen.

Fortunately, Ann exuded noticeably more friendliness than her husband had, making it easier for Raina to express her thanks for the housekeeper's efforts on her own and her relatives' behalf, but mindful of Dev's obvious desire to leave as soon as possible, of necessity she had to keep them short, and within ten minutes was presenting herself at the garage, as ordered.

Dev had already driven the vehicle out into the yard when she arrived, this time a mud-splattered Land Cruiser, but as she took her seat in the front Raina was surprised to find that they weren't only carrying her suitcase in the back, but half a dozen bright-eyed and happily chattering native children of varying ages as well.

'This is Miss Cameron, kids, a visitor from the big smoke, so just make sure you behave yourselves ... okay?' Dev addressed them with mock severity on seating himself behind the wheel. A statement that was received with much giggling and bobbing of heads. To Raina, he explained, 'Four of them are Ngarla and Daniel's grandchildren. The other two also have grandparents working on Alliance. I often take them with me for a visit when I drive over. You have no objections to them accompanying us?' His brows rose challengingly, almost as if he was expecting her to fault the arrangement.

'Naturally not,' she disclaimed in a slightly resentful tone as a result. 'In any case, whatever you choose to do on your property is your business, not mine!' An implicit attempt to make the point that what she chose to do was none of his concern either! Nonetheless, she was a little surprised that he had willingly burdened himself with the children in the first place. She hadn't imagined him the type to do such a thing.

From the brief, crooked upturn one corner of his firmly etched mouth assumed, she suspected her last words had succeeded in finding their mark, however, and hoped he would keep it in mind in future, despite him making no comment. He simply flexed a broad shoulder and checked to see that all those in the back were seated before beginning to drive past the rest of the outbuildings.

It wasn't long before they had left the homestead far behind and Raina soon became extremely pleased the children were with them as they kept exuberantly pointing out things of interest—a flock of long-necked brolgas she wouldn't otherwise have noticed in the long grass; rock wallabies perched in unbelievable positions high on a razorback—as they called the typically flat-topped hill they passed; a screeching flight of red-tailed, black cockatoos they disturbed in the midst of feeding; giant termite mounds and even more gigantic swollen trunked and bare-limbed boabs—and thereby saved her the necessity of making conversation with the man beside her.

After her experience of the day before, the road seemed in remarkably good condition to Raina and they were able to keep up a constant speed, but on presently coming across Bevan and another couple of men at work with heavy machinery, she suddenly realised the reason for the road's good surface. They were in the process of re-grading it. Stopping for a moment, Dev enquired as to how it was progressing, but on receiving evidently satisfactory replies they were soon on their way again.

Now travelling where the machines hadn't yet been, the road very quickly deteriorated to little more than a rough track, inevitably slowing their speed, but generating plenty of excited squeals and shrieks of laughter from those in the back when they were bounced off their seats or on to each other as the Cruiser lurched across stony creek crossings and jolted over rock strewn ruts.

'So what made you decide to be different and vote against the rest of them last night?' Dev caught her offguard by abruptly quizzing. 'As a sop to your conscience knowing it's going to be sold anyway?' His mouth shaped somewhat derisively.

'No!' Raina flashed him a indignant blue glance. Then wondering why she should bother defending herself to him, half shrugged and admitted in a quieter, fatalistic tone, 'Although I suppose that's all it will prove to have been in the end.'

'So it *was* purely in order to create an impression!'

'No, it was not!' Her temper flared involuntarily again. She wasn't accustomed to having her every move and decision dissected or criticised, and it riled that he should take it upon himself to do both. 'As I said then, I simply feel I'd like more time to think about it, that's all!' Her long lashed eyes rounded sarcastically. 'Is that such a crime?'

Ignoring the latter, he probed in a cynical vein, 'More time to think about what? How much the property means to you?'

'And is it so unbelievable that it *could* mean something to me?' she countered furiously.

'Quite frankly, considering your past record, yes!'

'What do you mean ... my past record?'

'Well, you could hardly say you've been a frequent visitor, now could you?' His slanted gaze was satiric.

Raina drew in a resentful breath. 'How could I be when it was made perfectly plain that none of us was welcome?'

'Including his daughter? His only child?' Punctuated with a short, disbelieving laugh.

'That's right, including me!' she gritted. Her expression became heavily overlaid with sarcasm. 'I may have been his only surviving child, but as you so rightly said, I was his *daughter*, and all my father was ever interested in was sons!'

Dev's lips curled scornfully. 'Is that what you've convinced yourself into believing ... to excuse your own shortcomings?'

'I don't need an excuse because it's all true!' she stormed. But on recollecting their passengers in the back, lowered her voice to add on a tartly smouldering note, 'I could tell how eager he was to see *me* from his one visit in sixteen years!'

'But still a hundred per cent improvement on your attempts to see him, hmm? So tell me, if he hadn't forbidden his relatives entry to Alliance—though I can quite understand why he wouldn't want such a pack of vultures anywhere near the place—would you have spared him the time from your butterfly existence to visit *him*?'

'Probably not,' she conceded with a perversely defiant toss of her head. 'He'd long ago made it patently obvious he wanted nothing whatever to do with me!'

'Which convenient contention then allowed you to wallow in self-pity to your heart's content ever since, of course,' Dev proposed scathingly.

Raina's eyes flared with bright sparks of indignation. 'I do not wallow in self-pity!' she denied hotly. Weren't there *any* faults he didn't ruthlessly intend to accuse her of having? 'And nor is it a contention, convenient or otherwise! Those happen to be the facts!'

'Except I happen to know differently.'

'Or mistakenly think you do, apparently!' she was swift to gibe. 'Not that it has anything to do with you, in any case!'

'Apart from an abhorrence at seeing a friend's lifetime of effort, together with his father's before him, squandered solely in order to expand the sybaritic lifestyles of his unappreciative and worthless relatives!' he retorted with undisguised contempt.

Since that particular aspect of the dissolution of the Estate had also been causing Raina some troubled thoughts, she didn't really feel able to dispute the point, despite knowing herself to have been included in the dununciation. However, there was one factor she wasn't averse to bringing up.

'Although only where I'm concerned, I note,' she sniped in caustic accents. 'I didn't see you condemning anyone else for their attitude . . . and particularly not

Adele when she was paying you such avid attention!'

'She's a very attractive woman,' Dev shrugged casually, and had Raina eyeing him caustically as a result. She supposed he had been flattered by her cousin's interest and therefore had found her outlook quite acceptable! 'While as for the others . . . after what Hayes told me about them, they merely confirmed his assessment of them, whereas *you*, his daughter,' the wealth of disparagement that suddenly hardened his tone had her literally flinching, 'couldn't even make it to his funeral on time! At least the rest of them managed to do that!'

'And so would I have done as well if I'd received notice of it earlier!' she defended fiercely. 'As it was, I think I did well to arrive when I did!'

The look he cast her was no less slighting than his previous words. 'Your telegram was despatched at the same time as all the others.'

'Except that I didn't happen to receive mine until late Tuesday afternoon!'

'You're trying to say it took longer to reach Perth than it did Sydney, on the east coast?' His dark brows arched with sardonic eloquence.

'No! Just that I happened to have been away from home at the time and wasn't informed of its arrival until I returned!'

'Away from home in some remote region where you just couldn't be contacted, of course.'

'Yes, I could have been contacted! I just wasn't, that's all!' Raina paused, beginning to chew at her lip. She was loath to explain her parent's thoughtless action in the matter, but under the circumstances felt she was entitled to all the same. With a hunching of one slender shoulder she disclosed in a reluctant voice, 'My mother assumed I wouldn't be interested in attending, so didn't bother to contact me.'

'An assumption made with good reason, though, presumably,' Dev surmised coolly.

Raina's temper rose uncontrollably once more. 'Considering the fact that I *am* here, plus the effort I did make to arrive on time, anyway, I would have thought I'd already put the lie to that with glaring clarity ... even for you!' she blazed, uncaring if the children in the back heard her now or not. 'So why don't you just mind your own business from here on instead of trying to fault me at every opportunity, huh?'

'Perhaps you just provide too *many* opportunities,' he goaded on a drawling note.

'Oh, go to hell!' she seethed, and refusing to dignify his comment any further, purposely swung her gaze away to stare unseeingly out of the open window. It was more than obvious he was determined to only see the worst, and she was damned if she was going to defend herself all the rest of the way to Alliance!

Fortunately, though, Dev seemed just as willing to leave matters as they were, at least for the time being, and they completed the remainder of the journey in silence, if a somewhat tense one, that was broken only by the children behind him asking the occasional question or, in Raina's case, pointing out more things of note.

The first time Raina actually realised they had crossed on to her father's property—although most stations in the Kimberleys contained some fenced paddocks, sheer size made boundary fencing out of the question—was when they passed a lily covered lagoon almost entirely ringed by cajuput trees, because, with a queer little start, she abruptly recalled having been there before. It was a peculiar experience, she discovered, to suddenly recognise something from so long ago and from so deep in her memory that there was no way she could have consciously pictured the scene, but from that point she started to take much more interest in her surroundings.

In fact, by the time the solid old mud-brick and stone homestead came into sight with its share of typically associated outbuildings, there had been a surprising number of places that Raina recognised, although now that they were so near to their destination all thought of those previous recollections fled as she concentrated on the oasis of green ahead.

There was the spreading poinciana where her first swing had been hung! she noticed with an unaccountable sensation of excitement. And in spite of being unable to see them, she just *knew* the cattle yards were behind that large new shed! The same as she knew instantly who that plump, motherly figure that had just emerged on to the verandah belonged to . . . Ngarla!

No sooner had Dev halted the Land Cruiser a short distance from the house than Raina was alighting as swiftly as the children in the back, but as they went scampering towards their grandmother she put a brake on her own steps and continued her approach at a more sedate pace. She wasn't a child any more, able to run to and throw her arms round the grey-haired woman on the verandah as she had used to, she reminded herself ruefully.

With a wide smile creasing her lined face, Ngarla bent to greet her grandchildren warmly and listen to the exited narration of their news. Then just as enthusiastically they were suddenly darting off again in search of their companions' grandparents, and as they departed an ebony gaze was focused on the girl now mounting the verandah steps.

'Welcome home, Miss Raina,' Ngarla said in her soft voice. 'It's been a long time.'

Raina nodded, feeling inexplicably selfconscious all

of a sudden. 'You didn't use to be so formal, Ngarla,'
she half lamented, half chided with a faltering smile.

Shining white teeth appeared in the beginnings of a
grin. 'You didn't used to come to me in such a
formal manner either,' the older woman half scolded
likewise.

Raina laughed and, the ice broken, moved forward
quickly to hug the plump figure before her. 'Oh,
Ngarla! It's so *good* to see you again!' she breathed
with fervent sincerity.

Still standing close, Ngarla raised a hand to lightly
touch the satin smooth cheek near hers. 'It's good to see
you too, Raina ... and so beautiful! You always were a
pretty child, and sort of delicate looking too. Only I
know you certainly weren't that, don't I?' she laughed
meaningfully. Then her expression sobered and she
sighed. 'If only Hayes had known as well.' Before Raina
had time to seek clarification of the remark that
brought a slight furrowing to her forehead, she went on,
'But how you've grown! You're taller than old Ngarla
now.' And smiling past her, 'You wouldn't know it to
see her now, Dev, but this girl only used to reach my
waist.'

From where he was leaning negligently against the
verandah post, Dev smiled ironically. 'She's been away
a good many years, Ngarla, and that's probably not the
only difference that's come about.'

Sensing more implied criticism, Raina stiffed a little
and half-turned to stare at him balefully as the woman
beside her continued. 'Well, I'm grateful to you for
bringing her to see me, and for bringing the children as
well. You're an all right feller.'

An assessment that had Raina grimacing inwardly,
but refraining from dissenting aloud. Besides, he *had*
brought her over, that much she was forced to admit.

For his part, Dev merely dipped his head wryly in

response. 'No sweat, the kids are never any trouble, you know that.'

Once again inferring that only *she* had been! Raina supposed vexedly.

'They also like coming with you, that's for sure,' smiled Ngarla, and then raised her brows enquiringly. 'You want to come in and have something to eat with us now, though, Dev? It's time for lunch.'

He shook his head. 'No, thanks, Ngarla. I'll go and have something with the men after I've taken Raina's luggage inside.' He began retracing his steps towards the Land Cruiser.

'You're staying?' The aboriginal woman swung to Raina with obvious pleasure lighting her eyes.

Raina nodded. 'For a couple of days . . . if you don't mind putting up with me for that long.'

'Not for good, then?' Some of the glow left Ngarla's gaze. 'I thought maybe Daniel had got it wrong when he told me Alliance was going to be sold.'

Her visitor looked away uncomfortably, her own demeanour losing some of its happiness also. 'No, he wasn't wrong, I'm sorry,' she sighed. 'The whole estate is to be sold eventually.'

'But if you said you wanted to stay here . . .'

'It wouldn't make any difference, I'm afraid,' was the dispirited reply. 'None of those eligible to run the estate are either interested, or capable of doing so.'

'Daniel mentioned something like that when he came home from the funeral but we couldn't understand,' Ngarla frowned.

'It's a long story,' Raina half smiled ruefully. 'But what it all boils down to is, I wouldn't be allowed to run Alliance, even if I did know how, because I'm not a man.'

'Huh! Plurry men!' ejaculated the housekeeper expressively. 'I've been running this homestead for

Hayes, and seeing he not bothered by any family squabbles from the men for over thirty years now and nothing go wrong! Why can't you do the same with the cattle? Daniel would help you. And so would Dev if we asked him, I'm sure.'

Raina somehow doubted Dev would feel inclined to do anything of the kind. Not that it had any bearing on the matter, in any event. 'Except that wouldn't be allowed either because they're not shareholders in the estate,' she had no choice but to squash the suggestion regretfully.

Ngarla heaved a partly disgruntled, partly fatalistic sigh and began leading the way into the homestead without further comment. Dev, it appeared, had already deposited Raina's case at the end of the hall and departed, so after directing one of the pretty, young house girls who assisted her in keeping the house spic and span to take it along to Raina's old bedroom, both of them adjourned to the large, old kitchen for a drink and something to eat as well as a long talk.

For Raina the remainder of the day turned out to be most enjoyable and relaxing, because once Ngarla had offered her condolences for the death of the younger girl's father, their conversation inevitably progressed to reminiscenses, a great many of them humorous, which seemed to roll away the years as if they had never been.

There was also a memory evoking tour of the homestead and its environs, and Raina was surprised at the number of people who had been on the station when she was a child and were there still. A lot of them, at least those somewhere around her own age, she could remember playing with, although they were employees now, but their presence did set her thinking.

'I notice there hasn't exactly been a high turnover of staff since I left,' she mused to Ngarla as they were returning to the house. Pausing, she tilted her head quizzically. 'Was my father a good man to work for?'

'One of the best!' came the immediate, categorical reply. 'Oh, he would shout and give the men curry at times, but they didn't care. They knew he'd never do anything wrong by 'em, and there's not one of us who wouldn't have done anything he asked, no matter what it was.' She pressed her lips together judiciously. 'And that Dev's another one of the same. His men both like and respect him too. That's why, if there's no work available here, our people go to Ajax Downs if they can. They know Dev's a top boss too. That's also why he and Hayes got on so good together. They were alike in lots of ways, those two.'

Meaning, the younger man was an unqualified male chauvinist as well? wondered Raina astringently. She wouldn't be a bit surprised! 'And—and Dev's as good a cattleman as my father was too, is he?' she suddenly found herself asking, although she couldn't really have explained why. Perhaps in the hope of uncovering an area where Dev Masters didn't excel. For at least where cattle were concerned she knew her father had been extremely successful because of the reports Charley provided the family with at the Estate's general meetings each year.

'Oh, yes,' laughed Ngarla, unaware of her companion's ensuing inward grimace. 'It was always a contest between the two of them to see whose stock topped the weights at the meatworks. Sometimes Hayes would win and sometimes Dev, and they were always roasting each other about the times the other lost.' She halted, her lined face slowly saddening. 'It won't be the same any more.'

Since she could offer no consolation for those forlorn words, Raina tactfully kept silent as she followed the older woman back into the kitchen where the two house

girls, Mabel and Ruby, were starting the preparations
for dinner. Their antics as they did so, however, soon
had all four of them bursting into laughter—like many
aboriginals, the two girls had a great sense of fun and
could find something amusing in the most mundane of
tasks—and which they were still doing when Dev put in
an appearance some time later with his six small
charges in tow to advise that he was about to leave.

'But I thought you'd be staying the night too!'
exclaimed Ngarla on hearing his intention. 'You often
have before, and I'm sure Raina was expecting you to.'

Raina certainly hadn't been anticipating any such
thing, and merely half smiled noncommittally.

'Ooh, yes, let's stay! Let's stay!' chorused the children
eagerly.

Dev flexed a broad shoulder and nodded to indicate
the small figures clustered about him. 'Their parents are
expecting them back tonight.'

In return, Ngarla sent him a half exasperated, half
threatening glance. 'You can radio them and let them
know what's happening,' she declared, indicating the
transceiver on one of the kitchen benches. Followed by
another mock menacing look for the still obviously
hopeful children. 'They'll probably be grateful for a
rest from these cheeky little fellers.'

Looking down at their expectant faces, he smiled
crookedly. 'I guess it would appear I've been outvoted,
wouldn't it?' Which brought forth more excited squeals
from the children until one glance from Ngarla
quietened them again. Then, eyeing his own drill-clad
length wryly, 'Although I'm hardly dressed for dinner.'

'Oh, there should be something of Hayes's in his
room that would fit you. You were much the same
height,' she easily found a solution to that problem.
'That is, if Raina doesn't mind.' She looked across the
table enquiringly.

On hearing her name mentioned, Raina dismissed her own deep thoughts with a start. 'What? Oh, no, I've no objections,' she averred, albeit a trifle distractedly, and abruptly surmising that she would probably be expected to sort out her father's effects of a personal nature. 'Provided, of course, that you don't object either.' She spoke directly to the man just inside the doorway for the first time.

'Not in the slightest,' Dev returned smoothly. 'I'd be proud to wear the clothes of such a man.'

The subtle nuance he managed to place on the word 'proud' had Raina lifting her slim, tip-tilted nose haughtily in the air and deliberately looking elsewhere, deciding that it had been yet another dig at herself, but on this occasion, rather than let him know it irritated her, tried to show that his opinions were of supreme indifference to her instead.

Whether she succeeded in her aim or not she didn't actually discover because with her gaze purposely averted she couldn't see his reaction. Nonetheless, even if did mean not finding out, she still wasn't entirely sorry when, shortly afterwards, the group in the kitchen began to disperse as they each began preparing for dinner and she could seek the seclusion of her own room.

Three-quarters of an hour or so later, after showering and dressing in the same simply styled blue and white silk dress with shoestring straps that she had worn the previous evening—she hadn't thought it necessary to bring many changes with her—Raina wandered along to the sitting room. But on finding she was the only one about, helped herself to a gin and lemon from the trolley beneath the window and, sipping at it slowly, made her way out on to the verandah.

Apart from the lights that were shining from various other buildings, it was pitch black outside, and for a few moments she stood quietly in the still, warm air, breathing in the scent of the land and listening to the sounds of the night. From the yards came the noise of penned cattle, followed by the barking of a dog, while from nearer at hand came the stirring of something amid the grass, the flap of an unseen bird's wings, and over all the ceaseless whirring of cicadas.

As had been happening all day, they evoked even more memories, tugging at both her conscious and subconscious senses, and as she took another mouthful of her drink Raina knew, all at once, that she just had to do something, anything, to prevent the ultimate disposal of the estate—and particularly Alliance. Too many sacrifices had been made, too many lives devoted to making it the property it was today, for all that to be wasted on outrageously unessential and purely pretentious schemes that would probably only satisfy for a few months before being carelessly discarded in favour of something else, she reasoned with strengthening conviction borne of past knowledge. No, she just couldn't allow that to happen, even if it meant she had to be the one to make sacrifices now to ensure the Estate's continuation. It simply meant more to her than she had ever before realised, she suddenly conceded.

But what sacrifices, and how? followed the desperate contemplation. That was her most pressing dilemma, and the one that occupied her thoughts totally for some long frowning minutes until one particular idea abruptly presented itself, and despite her initially dismissing it as completely unacceptable, kept returning to plague her.

No, she just couldn't! she repudiated vehemently. There were sacrifices and *sacrifices*, after all, and that one was just too much to ask! She would never be able to go through with it! Because she wasn't really prepared to be as selfless as she was trying to pretend for there had never been a time when she hadn't had to consider anything but her own wishes before? her brain taunted. The suspicion that that may have had an influence on her reluctance made her feel discomfited, as well as not a little guilty, and was eventually the cause of her suddenly squaring her shoulders defiantly. All right, she would do it! If the idea came to fruition and was successful, well and good, and if it didn't ... well, she would cross that bridge when she came to it!

About-turning determinedly, Raina returned to the sitting room and found Dev in the process of pouring himself a drink from one of the bottles arranged in the trolley. Dressed in a white shirt, complete with tie, and a pair of dark brown pants that fitted him remarkably well except for a slight fullness about his lithe waist and hips that denoted her father had been somewhat more solid in those regions, he seemed to fill the room with a vibrant masculinity that attacked Raina disconcertingly, and consequently had her draining her glass in an attempt to overcome it.

'I thought you must have still been dressing,' Dev opened the conversation casually as he put a cigarette to his lips and lit it. His eyes dropped to the now empty container in her hand. 'Would you like a refill?'

'Thank you. Gin and lemon, please,' she advised, taking the necessary paces forward in order to hand the glass to him. Picking up her own packet of cigarettes she had earlier left on the table, she lit one for herself while he was complying with her request. She had the feeling she might require the fortifying effects of both before the evening was out. Then, once again armed with a full goblet she took a deep breath, preparing to voice what was on her mind, but at the last moment just couldn't bring herself to say it and gave a shakily amused laugh instead as she gestured towards the formal dining room visible beyond a wide archway. 'It appears Ngarla means to serve dinner in style and we're to eat in solitary—or at least, dual—splendour.'

'Mmm, I suspected she might. In celebration of your homecoming . . . however brief.'

Rather than reply, especially in the fashion she felt inclined, Raina sipped at her drink, pretending not to have noticed that meaningful addition. She had more than enough on her mind as it was!

'I suppose you were also busy on the radio this afternoon arranging your flight back to Derby,' he went on to hazard in the same dry tone, and downed some of his own whisky.

Truth to tell, the idea hadn't once occurred to her, Raina abruptly realised, and shook her head. 'No, I wasn't as it so happens. In fact, that may even be unnecessary now. You see,' she took a deep, steadying draw on her cigarette, 'I—I've a business proposition I'd like to discuss with you.'

'Oh?' He viewed her keenly with deceptively lazy-lidded eyes. 'Such as?'

This time it was her drink Raina gulped at for courage. She couldn't get cold feet again now! 'Will you marry me?' she blurted, her cheeks colouring brightly. And if he dared say, 'I never knew you cared,' she just knew she would kill him!

He didn't, though. He merely eyed her with faintly whimsical humour—which was discomposing enough—and drawled, 'I thought you said a business proposition.'

'And so it would be! I'm talking about a marriage of convenience based solely on a platonic relationship, *nothing else*!' she hastened to convince him, wanting no doubts on that point. 'It appears my only means to prevent Alliance, as well as the estate's other assets, being sold.'

'In other words, you just need a male to run the properties for you, is that it?'

'In a nutshell!' Thank God he seemed to have got the gist of that!

'Leaving you free to return to Perth where the living's easy, while I'm left to do all the work in recompense for the dubious honour of being your husband, I suppose!' A decided sting entered his voice.

'No!' Raina gasped, shocked out of her brief feeling of satisfaction. 'I was intending to stay and—and help in any way I could. With—with the office work, or something like that, perhaps.' She hesitated, and then plunged on doggedly. 'At the same time, even though I'd be here, you would still be free to pursue as before your . . .' she swallowed heavily, her face staining once more, 'your—er—social life, or whatever, of course.'

'Thanks,' he acknowledged drily with a mocking dip of his head before seating himself nonchalantly on the arm of a chair and continuing to survey her flushed features intently. 'So why me?'

Raina felt too edgy to sit and walked across to the window. 'I—well—you were the one who accused me of leading a parasitic existence, so I thought you might be only too willing to help put an end to it,' she turned to quip somewhat glibly. 'Besides, you obviously know what running a station like Alliance entails, and—and such a marriage wouldn't entirely be unbeneficial to you either.' She gave a little shrug. 'I mean, instead of just being a manager for someone else, you'd be a part owner, wouldn't you?'

The curve of Dev's mouth became sardonically pronounced. 'In view of who the other shareholders are, you consider that a favour?'

His inherent mockery rankled and for the moment Raina forgot she was the one who wanted something from him. 'I don't see why not!' she flared. 'It's still better to be working for yourself than for someone else! And you'd have as good as sole control, anyway!'

'Except that I guess you could say I already happen to be working for myself,' he put forward on a wry note.

Twin creases of puzzlement made an appearance between Raina's glossily framed eyes. 'How do you mean? You said you managed Ajax Downs on behalf of the ... of the ...'

'Territory Pastoral Company?' he supplied with suspect helpfulness.

She nodded, tersely.

'And so I do,' he acceded indolently. 'It's just that when it was formed my family decided not to incorporate their name in its title as yours did with their Estate.'

'Oh!' For a time she didn't know quite what to say. This was something she hadn't foreseen! That a part ownership in the Cameron Estate would hold no interest for him because he already had a possibly even greater share in his own! If it hadn't been such a blow to her plans, she would have laughed at the comedy of it all. Instead, all she could do was to return his amused gaze rather resentfully and charge, 'Then if you had no intention of agreeing, you might at least have had the decency to tell me sooner!'

Dev drew on his cigarette and then dropped his dark eyes to its glowing tip. 'So who said I didn't intend to agree?'

'Well, do you?' Raina demanded sharply, wishing for once that she could see the expression in his eyes. It might have told her whether he was serious, or simply keeping her on tenterhooks for his own amusement!

'That depends,' he shrugged.

'On what?'

'Well, you could hardly claim that the marriages of the females in your family are known for their durability, could you?' Now he did look at her, mockingly. 'As I understand it, there's not one of them who hasn't been married at least twice.'

What he said was quite true, Raina was prepared to concede. Both her Aunt Olivia and her cousin Faith had been married twice, as well as her own mother, of course, while Adele had been through three husbands already. But what that had to do with the present situation she failed to see.

'So?' she queried with a touch of impatience.

'So I don't intend to have you running off for a divorce the moment the novelty of living up here wears off,' he announced in arbitrary tones. 'Because *if* we marry, we'll stay married! Got it?'

She hesitated momentarily and then nodded. After all, if it came to the worst there was always separation, which was almost the same. She took another sip of her drink, starting to feel more at ease about the matter already.

'Oh, yes, and there's one other condition . . .'

For some unknown reason, the sheer laziness with which the advice was imparted had Raina's stomach constricting involuntarily and her brief moment of complacency being replaced with a disturbing wariness. 'And that is?' she enquired tautly.

'It won't be a platonic relationship either,' Dev stated in a sardonic drawl.

'But—but it's supposed to be a business proposition!' she spluttered, aghast. 'And I said you—you'd still be free to come and go as you please.'

'Mmm, so you naïvely did,' he corroborated with a crooked tilting of his shapely mouth. 'However, although such an arrangement might work in the city, sweetheart, up here it's more likely just to be seen as me cheating on my wife, and there's no way I'm having that said about me. So if you want this marriage, then it will be one in the fullest sense of the word.' He raised a taunting brow. 'Or were you hoping to buy your way out of any responsibilities on your part, as per normal, with that share in the estate?'

Raina sucked in an indignant breath. 'No! And nor do I usually buy my way out of my responsibilities, or anything else for that matter!' she rounded on him heatedly. 'I just thought that, as a *business proposition*,' stressed pungently, 'a part ownership—not only in Alliance, but the Estate's other assets as well—would be more than adequate compensation for your part in the arrangement!'

'For taking on the added work of managing it, maybe,' he allowed. 'But for the added encumbrance of a doubtfully useful wife and her—umm—even less helpful relatives too?' Up went those ironical, goading brows again.

Unable to really dispute his latter estimation, Raina pounced on the former. 'What do you mean, doubtfully useful encumbrance?' she flared, taking strong exception to the description. 'I've offered to help in any way I can!'

'Mmm, I know, by doing the office work, and such. With which you've undoubtedly had a great deal of experience, hmm?'

'I—well—no, not really,' she was forced to confess uncomfortably. Her voice firmed again almost immediately. 'But I could learn! I'm not altogether lacking in intelligence! Or are you simply another of those men who, because they're afraid of the competition, like to convince themselves that a woman's only use is in the kitchen or the bedroom?' Her gaze was filled with derogatory sarcasm.

The long, leisurely, and explicit scrutiny he subjected her to had Raina reddening uncontrollably, much to her dismay and irritation. 'Not at all,' he finally denied, but on a faintly humorous note that only increased her annoyance instead of assuaging it. 'Although in your case, I guess you'd probably have to exclude the kitchen as well since it's extremely unlikely you've ever had any experience there either.'

He wasn't wrong, but then it wasn't her fault that her mother always employed a cook and a housekeeper. 'For all you know, the same might apply to the bedroom too, but you apparently don't consider that an encumbrance!' she gibed.

'It's you who suggested we marry, sweetheart,' Dev reminded with a shrug. 'And it's *your* relatives, not mine, that want to sell everything out from under you. That's just *my* condition for the marriage proceeding, that's all.'

'It's also blackmail!'

'Take it or leave it!' He flexed his wide shoulders indifferently again.

As well he might! fumed Raina, knowing he had her over a barrel. Of course, if she'd known anyone, anyone else *at all*, unmarried and possessed of the equivalent experience in managing a large grazing property she would have taken great delight in telling the arrogant Devlin Masters just what he could do with his condition! But she *didn't* know anyone else suitable, that was the problem, and if she refused to agree to his terms she would be right back where she started—with Alliance under threat. She sighed despondently. If she was truly determined to keep the Estate intact, it appeared she had no choice.

'You strike a hard bargain,' she accused bitterly.

'Meaning, you accept?'

'With the greatest of reluctance ... yes,' she grimaced.

A grin caught at his lips that infuriated her and she stubbed out her cigarette roughly. But at least the sudden rise in her emotions wasn't entirely without benefit, because it also engendered an accompanying determination not to meekly comply with that perturbing condition, but to thwart it in any manner she could. After all, she reminded herself with growing confidence, there had been other men in her life who had wanted to establish a physical relationship but who she had succeeded in keeping at arm's length without too much trouble, so why not Devlin Masters too?

CHAPTER FIVE

SINCE it was decided that it would perhaps be more prudent, from Raina's point of view at least, if her family weren't advised of her marriage until it could be presented as a *fait accompli*, she and Dev flew to Kununurra four days later for a private ceremony attended only by Charley Lawrence, who was to give the bride away, and his wife.

Fortunately, they arrived in town early enough for Raina to have time to purchase something suitable to wear, and at a small boutique she selected a finely pleated and delicately embroidered street-length dress of white organza, a pair of high-heeled sandals, and a wide brimmed hat that framed her delicate features perfectly, and which had a white rose tucked into its trailing chiffon band.

Dev, meanwhile, spent his time buying a ring, although when it came time during the ceremony for it to be handed to the minister, Raina was surprised to find that it was an identical pair that was passed across and not just one. So he meant to wear one too, she mused. She hadn't thought him the type. But perhaps she should have, came the prompt amendment, considering his expressed thoughts on marriage the night she had suggested the idea. Suddenly it made her feel somewhat guilty regarding her own casual attitude towards matrimony. Like the rest of her family, and possibly due to their influence, up until now she had always been inclined to treat it rather superficially too, she realised.

As a result of her contemplations, when the rings

were exchanged and their vows repeated, Raina
discovered herself to be markedly more affected by the
rite than she had anticipated. Somehow it made her
startlingly aware of the tall man at her side in a way she
had never experienced before, and for the first time she
began to wonder nervously just what she had started.

'You may now kiss your bride,' the minister's benign
voice abruptly cut into her reverie and, with a start, she
felt Dev's hand touch her chin and begin tilting her face
up to his.

No! There's no need for this! was her immediate,
panicking thought. We're not marrying for love! We're
only marrying for convenience! Then his dark head was
blotting out the sun streaming in through the windows
and his firmly moulded mouth was covering hers.
Momentarily, Raina's lips remained unmoving beneath
the light pressure, but then, to her utter mortification,
and considerable consternation, they waywardly began
to soften and respond. With a bright flush mounting
her cheeks she pulled away quickly and swung back to
face the minister, her heart pounding raggedly, and too
disconcerted to even look at her new husband again
until the necessary signatures had been provided and
they were back in the street again.

At one of the hotels in town they shared a late,
celebratory lunch with Charley and his wife, both of
whom seemed determined to view the marriage
romantically as a love match, somewhat to Raina's
surprise since she was positive Charley at least knew
otherwise. Just what Dev thought of the older man's
attitude, she couldn't be sure, but as he neither said nor
did anything to put the matter straight, she didn't
either, although she did question him about it once they
were airborne again some time later and heading for
Ajax Downs.

'Charley kept giving the impression that he thought

of the marriage as some sort of romantic elopement, although I'm not certain why,' she mused wryly as she removed her hat and combed her fingers through her silky, russet brown hair. She tilted her head quizzically. 'Or even why you didn't say something to disabuse him of the idea, if it comes to that.'

The corner of Dev's mouth that she could see turned upwards whimsically. 'In Charley's case, he was probably merely practising. In mine, I considered it best to follow suit under the circumstances.'

'Under the circumstances . . . practising?' she frowned. 'I don't follow you.'

He slanted her a heavily ironic glance. 'As you well know, your relatives aren't exactly going to welcome the news of your marriage, especially in view of how it will affect the Estate. In fact, they're undoubtedly going to be downright livid at having their schemes frustrated! So it's not unreasonable to assume they'll do everything in their power to find a loophole in order to circumvent such an obstacle, and if they could prove said marriage was an arrangement solely created for the purpose of preventing a sale, then that could just prove to be the excuse Steven will be searching for so diligently.'

'But I thought the terms of the Estate were water-tight!'

'So they would continue to have been . . . if you'd been married before your father died. But as it is, they may not be quite so secure if it can be shown to have been a purely obstructing move.' He paused, his lips shaping with rather grim humour. 'And in that regard, I might suggest you start doing some mental practising yourself, because unless I miss my guess, in the next week or so both you and Charley are going to be bombarded with some very irate accusations, as well as castigating communications, if not visitors.'

The former Raina had already anticipated, however

apprehensively, but . . . 'You think they're like to return *en masse*?' she gasped, wincing visibly at the thought. 'Couldn't you simply forbid them entry on to Ajax Downs? The same as my father did to Alliance?'

'I could, I suppose,' he concurred on a drawling note. 'Although whether they would accept such a ruling when something so important to them is at stake, is something else again, of course. In any event, I'm inclined to think that going to such lengths would only serve to convince them we could have something to hide.'

'And we don't?' she countered hollowly.

'Then maybe you *had* better start preparing, hmm?' His mocking eyes met hers briefly. 'Like you did during the wedding, for instance.'

Raina felt her face become washed with an embarrassed heat. Stupidly, apparently, she had hoped he hadn't noticed that discomposing response he had drawn from her. 'I—I'm glad you realised it was only for the sake of appearances,' she attempted to cover herself by dismissing it lightly. 'I wouldn't have wanted you to mistakenly believe it had been for any other reason.'

'I'll bear that in mind the next time it becomes necessary to—er—put on a show,' Dev averred in a distinctly sardonic overtone.

Surmising he hadn't been taken in at all by her parrying explanation, Raina averted her gaze hurriedly and turned it to the view below them instead.

'That isn't the Kununurra Diversion Dam still below, is it?' she promptly asked, not only as a means to change the subject but also out of interest. She was aware that Kununurra, meaning 'big waters', and the only new town in the Kimberley this century, had been built as the administrative centre for the Ord River Irrigation Scheme—provided by the damming of the largest river in the region—but the great expanse of blue water she could now see appeared much more extensive than she remembered Lake Kununurra being when they had flown over it that morning.

'No, that's the main storage area, Lake Argyle,' Dev explained. 'Its capacity is about nine SydHarbs.' Just about all water volumes of any size in Australia, including river flow rates, were measured against that of Sydney Harbour.

Raina nodded contemplatively. 'It's certainly huge,' she conceded.

'Mmm, filled to its maximum it covers almost a thousand square miles.' His lips curved ruefully. 'In our summer heat it also has an equally huge evaporation rate as well.'

'For example?' she half turned to probe.

'Around two thousand million cubic metres a year. Or put another way, around ten times the amount the city of Perth uses annually for domestic purposes.'

Raina released a long, expressive breath. 'Well, I suppose that's still better than letting it *all* pour out to sea as it used to before the dam was built,' she reasoned, swinging back to the window again and continuing her survey of the hill-dotted, and surrounded, lake until it eventually passed from view.

'By the way,' Dev began presently, and reaching into his pants' pocket withdrew a small, red velvet jeweller's box which he dropped lightly into her lap. 'I also bought that in town this morning. It seemed appropriate.'

'Oh?' She glanced at him curiously as she picked the box up and began to open it. 'For me?'

His mouth tilted lopsidedly. 'It sure isn't for me,' he drawled.

And Raina could understand why when she flipped back the lid. It was a magnificent diamond cluster engagement ring, the pattern on its wide gold band matching that of her wedding ring.

'It's beautiful,' she murmured sincerely, but suddenly feeling horribly selfconscious as she slipped it on to her finger next to her new wedding ring. It fitted perfectly. 'I—I really wasn't expecting an engagement ring too, but I do thank you. It's truly lovely.' She lifted her gaze to his with a somewhat shy smile.

For a moment their glances held, a fleeting expression Raina couldn't quite define appearing in Dev's, and then he was shrugging, 'I figured it would look more natural for you to have both if we're to convince people there's some feeling between us.'

Unaccountably, his explanation had some of her pleasure in the gift dissipating, though she did her utmost to both prevent it from showing, as well as to disregard it herself. 'Yes, of course,' she made herself agree with false brightness. 'How very sensible. It's just the thing to supply that added touch.' And once again she turned to concentrate her gaze outside the plane.

When they finally arrived at Ajax Downs, not surprisingly the news of their marriage spread like wildfire to everyone on the station, and during the next hour or so most of their time was spent in receiving and acknowledging congratulations. That Dev's staff, as Ngarla had contended, did indeed like and respect their boss became very evident to Raina during this period, and on one such occasion when he was speaking to one of the older stockmen she fell to watching him consideringly.

Once more she noted the impressive physique, the easy grace of his carriage, and the strong, devastatingly masculine features that had, at times, already had an inexplicable effect on her. Just as they were doing now! she abruptly recognised in dismay on finding her heartbeats quickening as a result of the lazy smile that was catching at his finely etched mouth.

For heaven's sake, get hold of yourself! she immediately censured inwardly. What are you trying to do? Make it easier for him when he's already made it plain he sees your part in this marriage purely as a convenient outlet for his own physical desires? It was the reminder she needed. Allowing her to overcome that momentary feeling of unruly attraction, but simultaneously causing her to ponder whether her plan for retaining the estate had been the right one all the same.

When the light began to fade, Raina and Dev at last returned inside the homestead in order to wash and change for dinner, but after mounting the stairs together Raina headed in the opposite direction to her husband, making for her own room, and then came to an astonished halt upon entering it. It was completely empty of any of her possessions!

Promptly, she stepped back into the hall to call after Dev urgently. 'What's happened to all my things? They've disappeared!'

As he about-faced she could see his white teeth flash in a wide grin. 'At a guess I'd say Ann and the girls have been busy since learning of our—umm—blissful tidings, and they've moved them all into the master bedroom.' Gesturing over his shoulder towards the room next to the one he had been about to enter.

'What!' Raina's almost shouted exclamation showed her agitation. Then swallowing heavily, she went on in what she hoped was a firmly decisive tone as she paced swiftly towards the room in question, 'In that case, I'll just return them to where they belong.'

'Uh—uh!' Dev stretched out a bronzed and sinewed arm to bar her way. 'They *are* where they belong.'

'No, they are not!' Anxiety had her voice rising a little again despite her defiant glare.

His return gaze was unyielding. 'And I said they were!' he mocked infuriatingly. 'The same as I also said this marriage of ours wasn't going to be a platonic one either.'

'You being eager to claim your so-called husbandly rights as soon as possible, is that it?' she gibed with an icy scorn.

'Whether I am or not has nothing to do with it! But use the master bedroom, you will!' Dev's own voice started to roughen now. 'Or do you think the most likely method to convince your relatives we're a loving couple is by occupying separate rooms?' The goading note returned.

Raina bit at her lip vexedly. 'But they're not even here!' she protested.

'Not at the moment, maybe, but once those wires go out tomorrow informing them of the situation, you're as aware as I am that that state of affairs could change very shortly!'

'S—so until it does, why . . .'

'Because in the meantime there are others here who also might find such circumstances somewhat odd,' he broke in satirically. 'And a carelessly imparted word at a later date could be exactly what *you* don't want, sweetheart. Just remember, it's your family estate that's on the line here, not mine!'

'So you keep saying!' she heaved helplessly.

'You can always arrange an annulment if you'd prefer.'

With a furious mutter beneath her breath, Raina pushed past him towards the master bedroom, knowing only too well—as she was sure he did too!—that having proceeded this far there was no way she would back down now. However, that didn't stop her sniping from the doorway, 'Compared to being forced to live as man and wife with you, even that could be eminently preferable!'

'Never mind, sweetheart,' he consoled on a taunting, laughing note. 'Who knows? You may even find yourself enjoying it.'

'Oh!' She sent him a baleful glare before storming into the room and slamming the door between them. The conceited baboon! she railed wrathfully. After having blackmailed her into this situation, did he really believe she would ever welcome his attentions? Hah! Didn't he have a lot to learn!

Looking about her cursorily at the pale lemon and white decorated room with its hand carved furniture and king size bed, which brought forth another disgruntled grimace, Raina kicked off her shoes and stalked across the rugstrewn, polished floor to begin removing her dress and silk slip, both of which she then tossed on to the end of the bed. Her hat, which she had left in the sitting room when they first returned, she now discovered to have already been placed in the top of the wardrobe where her own small selection of clothes was hanging. She would have to remember to ask in the telegram being forwarded to her mother for all her apparel, etcetera, to be forwarded by air, she mused. She was becoming tired of having nothing but the blue and white silk to wear for dinner every evening.

Moments later she was under the shower in the connecting bathroom, a somewhat larger one than that which had adjoined her previous room, and as the water cascaded over her head and shoulders it produced a relaxing effect which soothed her ruffled feelings to a large extent. At least, that was until she heard a sound on the other side of the tiled cubicle's partition and, on opening the sliding glass door a fraction, to her consternation found Dev calmly shaving with the aid of the mirror above the double vanity unit, his only apparent covering a loosely fastened towel about his lithe waist.

'What the hell are you doing here?' she exploded indignantly. 'Can't you grant a person just a little privacy? Go and use your own bathroom!'

'Since there isn't one next door, this always has been my bathroom,' he claimed without taking his eyes from the task in hand. 'While as for privacy ...' his lips twitched with an evident amusement that promptly set Raina's emotions smouldering, 'well, I guess once you're married you have to expect to lose that to some extent. In any case, you're certainly not the first female I've seen unclad or otherwise, so I'm not likely to lose control at the sight of a naked woman. Even one with your,' he paused, and now he did half-turn in her direction to run a measuring gaze the length of her, making her embarrassedly aware that the glass of the shower screen, although amber in colour and rippled, still wasn't altogether opaque, 'obviously enticing shape.'

Reddening uncontrollably, Raina thrust the door shut again, deducing nothing she could say would succeed in removing him from the room, and continued with her shower with as much composure as she could manage, but ensuring her back was turned to him the whole time nonetheless. When she eventually finished she opened the door a crack again, reaching with a slender arm for the fluffy green towel on the rail outside, and hastily dragging it through the opening and wrapping it about herself securely before finally stepping out of the cubicle. Intending to dry herself in the bedroom—she wasn't going to remain in there with him any longer than was absolutely necessary—she made for the doorway with her head held high. Only to discover it abruptly being tilted even higher as Dev's hand grasped her about the chin when she would have passed him.

'Don't you think you're slightly overdoing the

blushing modesty bit?' he drawled wryly. 'When all's said and done, we *are* married ... and at your suggestion.'

Did he have to keep reminding her—of both facts! 'You also knew I objected to this—this sort of marriage!'

His fingers moved evocatively against the soft, exposed skin of her throat and she swallowed hard. She had never felt more vulnerable in her life! 'Although you did agree.'

'Under duress!' she retorted acrimoniously, trying desperately to submerge her sense of assailability beneath a bolstering rancour. 'The same way it will have to be to make me share that bed in there with you!'

'Oh?' His brows peaked in goading unison. 'You're partial to a little rough stuff, are you?'

'No!' she gasped, appalled. How could he even think such a thing?

'Then I suggest you stop issuing challenges that can only end in that fashion,' Dev counselled with an aggravating tap to her chin in emphasis and, releasing her, stepped towards the shower, unfastening his towel as he went.

His action effectively put paid to Raina staying to add anything further for she immediately made herself scarce by hurrying into the bedroom. He had done that on purpose, simply to make certain he had the last word! she seethed impotently as she began drying herself. He was nothing but an autocratic, overbearing, and thoroughly objectionable brute! But if he was so keen to have the last say then he could have it—at least for now, she decided acidly. Because by the time he finished his shower, she meant to have long since left the bedroom.

Speculating that it was probably the fastest she had ever dressed, Raina still only just managed to make it into the hallway before Dev emerged into the bedroom. But she had made it, even though with still noticeably damp hair, and as a result there was a satisfied lightness in her step as she descended the stairs and headed for the billiard room.

Joe was the only one there when she arrived, and although she could have wished for Bevan's less dour presence, she smiled her thanks with equal warmth as if it had been the younger man when the lean and laconic overseer poured and handed her drink to her. After a few minutes spent trying to engage him in social conversation, though, she soon realised she was achieving nothing but her own frustration and, deciding now was as good a time as any to get the problem out into the open since they were alone, took the bull by the horns.

'You don't approve of me, do you, Joe,' she began by declaring rather than questioning in rueful tones.

His brown eyes widened minimally in surprise before he dropped them to his drink and gave an impassive shrug. 'It's not for me to approve, or disapprove of you.'

'That still doesn't prevent you from having an opinion, though, does it? And I suspect that, for some reason, it isn't a particularly high one where I'm concerned, unfortunately.' She paused. 'So don't you think I'm at least entitled to know why?'

'Why should you care?'

Raina sighed. It was like trying to get information out of an oyster. 'Because if I'm going to be living here, I should think it would be more comfortable, for everyone, if we could *all* converse in a natural manner. You seem to get on well enough with everyone else and I'd like us to as well. Besides,' she half smiled diffidently, 'if I'm going to be judged, I'd like to know what for.'

Joe took a swift mouthful from the glass in his work roughened hand. 'You left your father to rot without even so much as word in all the time you were gone!' he castigated abruptly. 'And what's more, I wouldn't put it past you to do the same to Dev if it suits you! I may only be an ignorant bushman, but I don't need anybody to tell me that this sudden marriage of yours isn't all it's supposed to be! Dev means nothing to you! I don't know how, but it's my guess you're just using him for your own purposes!' he hesitated, his gaze holding hers grimly, then continued regardless. 'But if you do treat him the same as you did Hayes, then I give you fair warning, you won't want to show your face in the Kimberley again because there won't be a person here who won't have it in for you! Dev's as good a man as they make, and you're lucky to be married to him—I know plenty who'd give their eye teeth to change places with you—so you keep that in mind and don't do him any bad turns and maybe in time you and I'll get along just fine too.'

Well, she had asked for the reasons behind his disapproval, and she'd certainly been given them—with both barrels! thought Raina with a gulp for the vehemence with which they'd been delivered. And she'd supposed him to be laconic! followed the ironic recollection.

At the same time she was also somewhat guiltily aware that she *had* considered separation as a means of escaping her arrangement with Dev, and nor did she think anything she could say in defence of her marriage was likely to convince Joe it had been the result of a whirlwind romance. But as for his remarks regarding her father, they had both hurt and caused a feeling of resentment. The more so because Dev had already voiced the same sentiments, and also because she was now beginning to suspect that the reserve with which she had been treated by her father's friends at the funeral had been for the same reason, and not due to her late arrival as she had believed at the time. Now, with a defiant lift of her chin it was to his first point that she chose to refer.

'By the same token, it could also be said that my father left me to rot without so much as a word since I don't remember him ever displaying any interest in contacting me either!' she had no compunction in retorting.

If possible, Joe's expression became even more disparaging. 'No? You're forgetting that trip of his to Perth, aren't you? The one he told all and sundry hereabouts was for the sole purpose of attempting to re-establish contact with you, and to see if you couldn't be persuaded to spend some time up here, at least during your holidays!'

'Then he lied!' she asserted on a flaring note. 'He never said more than a couple of words to me, and he certainly didn't mention anything about spending time at Alliance!'

'If he didn't, maybe that was because you apparently made it plain right from the minute he arrived that you wanted nothing to do with him!' he put forward in rather sardonic accents.

'That's unfair!' Raina immediately charged. 'He could hardly have expected me to welcome him with open arms, as it were, after he'd always made it obvious I was of very little importance to him due to my being a girl! In any event, I was only eleven at the time, and after an absence of five years I could only just remember him.' She expelled a heavy breath, her features clouding pensively. 'Apart from that, to be quite honest, he terrified me. I remember thinking that he always seemed to be judging me . . . and finding me wanting,' she interposed, protectively flippant, 'the way he loomed over me. He never used to talk to me or play games with me as he did with my brother, so when my mother called me into the sitting room without warning that day he visited us and I saw him there, still towering over me and still looking at me as if I'd failed to come up to his expectations in some way, naturally I didn't exactly react to his unanticipated appearance with joyful exuberance. I simply preferred to remain very much in the background and out of his way.'

'And thereby succeeded in making him believe he'd lost all hope of reestablishing any sort of relationship with you,' came the comment in Dev's voice from the doorway behind her, and which had her whirling to face him defensively. His remark had sounded accusing. She also wondered just how much he had heard.

'Well, that wasn't my fault!' she protested. 'I didn't even realise he wanted any contact with me! Although that was probably only because Clark wasn't still alive!'

He tut-tutted half reprovingly, half provokingly, as he paced lithely into the room, his movements unconsciously filled with a virile strength and vitality. 'Self-pity, kitten?' he chided in a drawl.

'No, just an educated deduction in view of the known facts,' she contradicted bittersweetly, mindful of Joe's presence.

'Except that the facts are, as I've been led to believe, that the reason he treated you so differently to your brother was because he also happened to have been extremely nervous of you.'

'Of *me*?' Raina repeated in astonishment, and then uttered a scoffing laugh. 'Why? What did he think I was going to do ... bite him on the ankle?'

'It may have been better if you had,' he acceded somewhat enigmatically as he crossed to the bar to splash some whisky into a glass and down a portion of it before actually answering her facetious question.

'Because he was simply a big, gruff—you might even say, somewhat inarticulate—man at times who just felt completely out of his depth when dealing with his beautiful and so fragile looking daughter. He was always a man who felt more at ease in the company of other men, and so when your brother came along, who was of a much sturdier build evidently, it was just a case of Hayes being able to relate to him more easily, that's all,' he revealed quietly.

The colour drained from Raina's face. 'Is that the truth?' she sought confirmation on a gasped note, looking from one to the other of them distractedly. When they both nodded in turn, she shook her head in despair. 'But I wasn't fragile, even if I did look it! Why didn't somebody tell him?'

'Ngarla tried, but unfortunately he just couldn't see it that way,' Dev advised. 'To him, you were a delicate little doll he was frightened would be hurt, or break even, if he treated you in the same manner as he did your brother, and so he left you to be raised by your mother, thinking that was best for you.'

'Then why didn't she tell him differently?'

He looked down at his drink, shrugging. 'From what I can gather, her main concern was in returning to the social life in Perth.'

'But she always claimed his lack of attention to me was because I'd been born the wrong sex!'

'Perhaps she believed it was. As I said, Hayes was never a man who found it easy to put his feelings into words . . .'

'He seems to have managed to with you, though, apparently!' she cut in somewhat accusingly.

'Once again . . . as I also mentioned before, he was always more comfortable among men,' Dev reminded patiently. 'But just because he found it difficult to express his feelings, that didn't mean there weren't any there. And since, within a few months of marrying him, your mother discovered that living on a large property in the far north wasn't quite the romantic picnic she had obviously imagined it was going to be . . .'

'And never stopped complaining thereafter!' It was Joe who interrupted him this time, darkly, causing Raina to glance up at him with a meditative frown.

'Then I doubt the atmosphere between them would have been particularly conducive to heart-to-heart discussions, in any case,' concluded Dev.

Raina sighed disconsolately, knowing from statements her mother had often made that he was more than likely correct, but it was on the older man that her attention became fixed. 'Did you know my mother, then, Joe?' she quizzed.

'Only on a nodding basis. Your mother always believed in keeping herself apart from the staff,' he disclosed in dry tones. 'But I'd sometimes see her when she came visiting. Ann and myself came to work at Ajax Downs a couple of months before your parents finally split up.'

'So you would've known me too, I suppose, as I understand she used to bring me over here with her,' Raina surmised.

'No, I can't really say I knew you because I only ever actually saw you the once. The day you fell off the tank stand,' he divulged with a sudden, unexpected grin, and had her blue eyes widening. Her mother had never told her about that. 'And what a commotion that created! You weren't really hurt—just bruised and scratched, and shaken up a bit, that's all—but to have heard your mother carry on you'd have thought you'd broken every bone in your body. As far as she was concerned, it was just another reason for leaving the north. She couldn't seem to appreciate that when kids start climbing they've just as many opportunities for accidents in the city as they have in the bush.' He paused, his expression becoming whimsical. 'It was a pity Hayes wasn't here that day to see you. That might perhaps have convinced him you were a good deal stronger than you looked, because you just took it all in your stride. It was your mother who couldn't come to terms with it.'

With a dismal half nod, Raina began moving towards the doors that led on to the verandah, her eyes bright with unshed tears. Oh, God, what a tragic series of mistakes and misunderstandings! she despaired. If only her father had explained, or her mother not been so quick to condemn! Or even if Ngarla had succeeded in convincing him that his daughter had been no less strong than any other child on the station. She supposed that must have been what the housekeeper had been referring to that day when she visited Alliance.

'Maybe he should have remembered there was at least fifty per cent of himself in you, hmm?' Dev's deep voice abruptly sounded close beside her as he dropped an arm about her shoulders and drew her comfortingly, unresistingly nearer.

'Mmm,' she sighed sadly. 'Davey Newell, the pilot of my plane, said I looked a little like him.'

'Only much more beautiful, of course,' he complimented with a smile, obviously trying to lighten her mood.

As she remembered, Davey had said something similar to that too, except he had said 'prettier'. Strangely, the fact that Dev should have been the one to call her beautiful seemed to hold more significance for her than it warranted, especially since he was evidently only attempting to make her feel better. In consequence, she merely gave a weak, non-committal smile in response.

Exhaling ruefully, Dev rubbed a hand around the back of his neck. 'While we're still on the subject, however, I guess this is as appropriate a time as any for me to apologise for giving you such a rough time the day of the funeral. I'm sorry, I just didn't realise you'd been labouring under a misapprehension all these years as well.'

'It appears we all were,' she allowed in choking tones and brushed the back of her hand across her suddenly wet lashes.

'Hey! Come on now, sweetheart, no tears,' he urged soothingly, tipping her woebegone face up to his with his free hand. 'You really should be pleased rather than sad at having your beliefs proved wrong at long last, you know.'

'I—I am,' she owned tremulously. 'It's just that I wish . . .'

'Good evening, all! I'm sorry to be late but I didn't get finished until just on dark. Is there still time for me to have a drink?' Bevan's breezy entrance into the room had Raina halting and trying desperately to achieve a more composed state before turning to acknowledge his presence.

As it happened, his arrival coincided with Ann's from the kitchen and it was she who answered his question. 'No, sorry, you'll have to miss out tonight, Bevan, as dinner's just about ready,' she smiled. 'You'll have to make do with the wine with your meal instead.'

'Champagne, I trust, since we've something to celebrate this evening,' he promptly grinned. Then, with a speculative look in Dev and Raina's direction, 'Although it beats me why you're not on honeymoon.'

'That's probably because it takes very little to beat you, young feller, so why don't you just head into the dining room and mind your own business, huh?'

retorted Joe gruffly, giving the young jackaroo a light push in the back to propel him on his way.

With an offhand shrug, Bevan did as ordered, but with something of a scowl on his face which took Raina by surprise and thereby had her forgetting her own disappointments for the moment. She had expected him to accept the censure, particularly as it had been delivered in a more or less bantering fashion, with better grace than that. Now it appeared he might not always be quite so cheerful and good-natured as she had previously thought.

'Are you sure you feel up to celebrating?' Dev bent to query as they too began moving.

Unable to determine from his tone whether he was meaning she probably didn't consider their marriage something to celebrate, or because of the distressing revelations concerning her father, after a moment's contemplation she surmised it was more likely to be the former and reacted accordingly.

'I'll manage,' she contended with her head angling to a challenging level.

But despite her confident reply, Raina found it almost impossible to do justice to the beautiful meal that Ann had obviously prepared especially for the occasion, or to participate with anything like her normal spontaneity in any of the general conversations that occurred while her mind was so filled with more perturbing thoughts. As a result, she couldn't have been more thankful when, shortly after coffee had been served in the sitting room, the others discreetly took their leave—presumably believing she and Dev would prefer to be on their own, she supposed sardonically— because it also enabled her to plead tiredness and retire to the seclusion of her bedroom without creating any surprised conjecture.

Once there, though, the tears of regret that had made

their brief appearance before dinner and been valiantly suppressed, now welled uncontrollably into her eyes as she prepared for bed. 'If only ...' were the two words that seemed to prefix her every thought, each time bringing new trails of dampness to her pale cheeks, and making her despair so anguishedly that it wasn't possible to turn back the clock for even a short while, that after finally climbing miserably beneath the covers of the wide bed, her pillow was soon almost as wet as her face.

A while later she heard Dev moving around in the next room and found herself tensing involuntarily. He couldn't possibly be intending to claim his marital rights tonight, of all nights, could he? Surely he would allow her time to at least *try* and become accustomed to the idea! Then, as the minutes lengthened and he made no appearance, she began to relax slightly again, although only to leap into a sitting position with a start about half an hour later, the sheet clutched to her protectively, when a summary knock on the door connecting the two rooms preceded its opening—without waiting for any sanction in her part, she noted rancorously—and Dev walked calmly into the room. That he was still dressed in the same clothes he had worn at dinner did permit her to eye him a little less apprehensively, however, even if it didn't make her feel better disposed towards his uninvited entrance.

'Are you okay?' he asked watchfully, taking in her discernibly tearstained countenance at a glance.

'Yes, thank-you,' she said primly with a sniff, just wishing he would leave, but disarmed a little by the concerned note in his voice nonetheless.

His mouth twisted wryly for a second as he casually, arbitrarily seated himself on the side of the bed. 'You don't look it,' she was informed in expressive accents.

Raina edged away from him surreptitiously and

hunched a slim, lace covered shoulder. 'It—it all came as something of a—a shock, that's all.'

'I know,' he owned in an unexpectedly deep tone. And reaching out to touch her still damp cheek with gentle fingertips, 'But Hayes would have been the last one to have wanted to see you made so unhappy by it, you know.'

'M-maybe.' She had to bite at her lower lip to stop its ungovernable trembling. 'It's just that all my life I've been led to believe he didn't want anything to do with me, and then to discover that wasn't true, but only when it's too—too late to do anything about . . .' She came to a shaking halt, her eyes veiled with tears once more, her hands clenching helplessly. 'Oh, God, why didn't he try to contact me again when I was older . . . write to me, or something? Why didn't I make an effort to contact him as I sometimes thought of doing? If only someone had told me a year, a month, a week ago even! At least then I would have had a chance to see him again! Now it's too late and I'll never be able to explain!' She couldn't control the grief stricken sob that escaped her.

'Oh hell, Raina, don't!' Dev groaned, drawing her within the circle of comforting arms compulsively, her head coming to rest weakly against the solid wall of his chest. 'You may not be able to explain but, believe me, you've done the next best thing! You've kept the Estate intact, as he always hoped and prayed you might, and which just about more than anything meant the world to Hayes.' He brushed a hand soothingly over the silky fall of her hair. 'So don't ever cry for what might have been, sweetheart, because I've no doubt he's at peace just knowing Alliance evidently does mean as much to you as it did to him.'

Drawing a shuddering breath, she lifted a wistful gaze to his for reassurance. 'Do you really think so?'

'I reckon,' he half smiled softly as he dropped a feather-light kiss on to her forehead.

How she wished it could be true! 'But if only . . .'

'No more "if onlys",' he broke in with a vetoing shake of his head. And momentarily there weren't as his mouth briefly took possession of hers this time. 'Unfortunately they can't undo the past, and you'll only succeed in upsetting yourself more if you continue thinking that way.'

Distracted a little by his kiss, although not diverted by it, Raina now shook her own head—but somewhat tearfully. 'I would so like to have had a chance to at least *see* him once more,' she cried.

'I know, sweetheart, I know,' Dev sighed, cupping her troubled face within his palms and kissing away the new tears from her cheeks.

Unaware how it quite happened—had she unknowingly sought his, or vice versa?—Raina suddenly found his mouth covering hers once more, but this time it lingered persuasively and, as had occurred in church that morning, her own lips began to cling in return as if of their own accord. Only now she didn't pull away as she had then, but rather savoured the feel of the sensuous contact, her desolated emotions seeming to welcome this new outlet for the release of their fervent expression.

There was an increasing insistence, an overpowering demand in his kisses that she responded to unreservedly, unconsciously, and which sent a consuming fire sweeping over her body. She was aware of him, of his tautly male outline, as she had never been of any man before, and in turn equally aware of her own desires as never before. Pushing aside the lacy top of her nightdress, Dev covered the creamy skin of her shoulder thus exposed with his caressing mouth and Raina felt an unruly wave of wanting surge through her. A need she inexplicably felt only his complete possession could fulfil.

Abruptly raising his head, Dev looked down at her with eyes darker than usual as he murmured unevenly, 'I want you, Raina!'

Under the impact of his tense gaze her heart hammered wildly. 'I know,' she whispered on a husky, yielding note as she selfconsciously reached up to undo those buttons that were fastened at the neck of his silk knit shirt.

Swiftly diversing himself of his clothes, Dev was soon sliding his tall, hard length next to hers, his hands gentle but deft as they disposed of her shielding nightwear. Then gathering her back into his arms, the touch of his firm, muscular frame against hers stirring her senses to new heights, he proceeded to arouse her even further with both his exciting mouth and his knowing hands as they explored every part of her quivering body with an expertise that turned her blood to fluid fire and had her responding with a wanton exhilaration.

Emboldened by the overwhelming feelings Dev's intoxicating exploration had galvanised into life, Raina experienced the need, the wish, to know his powerful shape better too, and so she allowed her hands to wander shyly from the strong contours of his heavily muscled back and shoulders to his no less rugged chest, his taut and flat stomach, his lean and supple waist. With a muffled groan, his mouth recaptured hers hungrily, his hands slipping down her back to her curving hips, pulling her closer. Pressed against his wide chest, Raina's breasts ached with desire, and as if realising it, Dev turned his attention to them, his lips and tongue tantalising her already prominent nipples with their inflaming attentions until, arching to meet him feverishly, she gave a soft moan of shuddering pleasure.

Dev moved slightly, and Raina accepted the feel of his hard thighs against hers willingly, only shrinking away momentarily from the swift, sharp pain that followed as his aroused body claimed total possession of hers, and then moving with him until simultaneously they reached a peak of almost unbearable ecstasy that left her feeling shaken and limp.

Afterwards, with their legs still entwined, she lay with her head resting against his shoulder, her eyelids heavy with the aftermath of passion, his arms wrapped about her securely. She would never have believed she could feel quite so exhausted, or so . . . contented? she mused drowsily before gradually drifting into a deep and dreamless sleep.

CHAPTER SIX

ON regaining consciousness the following morning, however, Raina was in nowhere near such a relaxed state of mind as she had been those last minutes before falling asleep in Dev's arms the previous evening. There may only have been an indentation in the pillow beside her to remind her what had occurred—he had obviously awoken much earlier than she had, for which she was now extremely thankful—but that was enough to have her throwing an arm across her eyes in a gesture of despairing consternation as she lay back on her pillow.

Oh, God, no matter how sorrowful the disclosures regarding her father had made her feel, how could she possibly have permitted those emotions to have been channelled into such an extreme form of physical release! It may have succeeded in providing a kind of balm for her bruised spirit at the time, but now all she felt was embarrassed and cheap! Dev didn't love her, and to him it had undoubtedly merely been a convenient method of achieving physical satisfaction— the light in which he had viewed their marriage all along—but what perhaps caused her the most mortification was the knowledge that he was all too aware that she didn't love him either! So just what did that make her, for not only having succumbed to his lovemaking when no such emotion had been involved, but for actually having responded to it so eagerly and so uninhibitedly? She squirmed inwardly with humiliation, hating to think.

A few meditative minutes later, Raina threw off the covers and set her feet to the floor determinedly. Well, there was only one thing for it! Hiding in her room, despite its obvious appeal, wasn't going to solve anything. She was just going to have to brazen it out with as much aplomb as she could muster, and while so doing ensure it became unmistakeably evident that it had simply been a fleeting transgression on her part that was never likely to be repeated!

With this firmly in mind, Raina made her way down the stairs decisively a little while later, resolved to seeing Dev without delay in order to set matters straight. And thereby also hopefully relieve her of most of the feelings of selfconsciousness she was still disconcertingly experiencing. A plan she had no choice but to postpone, she soon discovered to her vexation on being advised by Jean, the house girl who served her breakfast in the dining room, that Dev had left the homestead more than an hour before in company with a couple of the men to check the holding yards at the Bauhinia Bore and wasn't expected to return until some time in the afternoon.

Having been all prepared for the meeting, the information came as something of an anti-climax and Raina finished her solitary meal in a rather disgruntled mood. Not the least of her dissatisfaction concerning just how she was expected to fill in her day until her husband returned! He might at least have had the forethought not to disappear quite so early on the first day after their marriage without giving *some* clue as to how she might occupy her time! After all, he had been the one to always accuse her of living a useless life. Now it appeared he was doing his best to see it continued along the same lines!

Remembering her own comments on the subject, Raina searched out the office after breakfast, intending to see what she might perhaps be able to attend to in there. She found it at the back of the house, a not particularly large room containing a couple of heavy wooden desks and chairs together with an assortment of associated office equipment, including a typewriter, and the walls of which were adorned with more rifles; a few photographs of impressive looking cattle; and a coloured map of the property with its various paddocks outlined thereon, as well as showing the locations for - each of the holding yards, bores, creeks, waterholes, lagoons, etcetera, the whole intersected by a maze of winding tracks and roads.

Both desks were half hidden beneath piles of paper, folders, and mail—both opened and unopened—she noted with a somewhat satisfied smile, and heading for the largest of them she immediately set about preparing to prove her point that even without prior office experience she could do *something* to help. Nevertheless, after an hour or more of concentrated reading and attempted sorting, Raina was reluctantly forced to admit that she was getting nowhere fast. And it wasn't altogether due to her lack of knowledge regarding office procedures either, she defended ruefully. It was mainly because she just had no idea as to how Dev preferred to deal with it.

For instance, where trade papers, magazines, and circulars were concerned—did he keep them, or read and dispose of them? Letters requesting donations and subscriptions—did he contribute to all, some, or none of them? Then there were the invoices, personal letters—which she hadn't read once she realised that's what they were—and quotes for assorted potential purchases. Did it really cost *that* much for each mile of fencing? And no wonder no one on large properties ever bothered to erect boundaries when it would apparently cost a cool million just to have them surveyed!

With a defeated sigh she turned her attention to the typewriter, but after having proved to herself that even she could type with two fingers if it became necessary, her interest soon waned due to having nothing specific to which she could apply that level of ability, and with another heaved breath she wandered outside.

For the remainder of the day, Raina ambled around acquainting herself with each of the outbuildings and their functions, talking to the old gardener who lavished such care on the station's fruit and vegetable produce, and discussing with Ann the general aspects of running the homestead. That any help from her in this area really wasn't necessary was quite obvious because the housekeeper, together with her three helpers, already had it down to a fine art, but she thought it as well to know something of what was required, and besides, it helped to fill in another hour or so.

Dev arrived back just before four, and as she happened to be looking over the machine shed at the time, Raina watched him and the two men with him dismount and begin unsaddling their horses with an increasing annoyance. Oh, yes, she supposed he had reason to look in such good spirits! He'd had something to occupy his mind all day! It was just herself who'd been left to do absolutely nothing!

'Hi! What are you doing down here ... repairing the equipment?' her husband teased in surprise on seeing her as he began heading for the house. 'Did you have a good day?'

He couldn't have asked a worse question considering how she was feeling, although conversely it did allow her to return his amused glance without any trace of the selfconsciousness that might otherwise have been present. 'No, I did not!' she retorted fierily, moving into step with him. 'And the reason I was in the machine shed was because I was trying to find something to occupy my mind just so I wouldn't die of boredom!'

'Already?' His brows arched explicitly, his expression

assuming a distinctly more watchful cast. 'Even your mother took longer than a day to start missing the bright lights of the city.'

'The city has nothing to do with it!' Raina fumed. He *would* choose to put that construction on it! 'But if she didn't, then maybe my father was at least considerate enough not to simply disappear and leave her without a damned thing to do all day!'

He flexed a muscular shoulder impassively. 'In view of how you were obviously feeling last night, I thought you may have preferred to take it easy today.' A reminder that had a faint, but still uncontrollable flush staining her cheeks. 'However, if doing something was so important to you, you could always have tried the office ... as I recall you vehemently claimed you intended.' His voice became shaded with a drawling mockery.

'And as I did try! But without any prior knowledge as to just how you deal with your correspondence, I soon discovered how futile an exercise that was!' Her own voice wasn't completely free of sarcasm now either. Then sucking in an encouraging breath, she intrepidly concentrated her thoughts on his first remark, deciding that since he had brought the matter up, even if only indirectly, the sooner she made her position clear in that regard the better, for both of them. 'While as for last night, I guess your and Joe's revelations must have upset me more than I realised, and as a result I unfortunately reacted in a rather—rather over-emotional manner. I'm sorry. It won't happen again, I can assure you.'

'Is that so?' A sardonic curve swept Dev's mouth upwards.

'Yes!' she stated unequivocally, determined there should be no misinterpretation despite suspecting his response hadn't really been meant as a question. 'But to return to more significant matters . . .' Her words were deliberately selected. 'Perhaps if you could just spare me a few minutes of your valuable time this evening in the office, in future I won't have to spend the whole of my days floating around like some piece of superfluous flotsam!'

'Jetsam,' he corrected on a goading note that was repaid with a fulminating blue glare.

'Well, whichever! So are you going to show me what needs to be done, or aren't you?'

'Since you're plainly anxious to make yourself indispensable, why not? You can even try your hand with Alliance's books as well if you're so keen, seeing we'll be responsible for those too from now on.'

Raina surmised he was mocking her again and retaliated accordingly. 'It can only be an improvement on the *duties* I've been allowed to perform to date!' she gibed with acid inference.

For a moment Dev's eyes grew distant, and then their dark depths abruptly shone with a taunting lustre. 'Although in view of the—er—unrestrained fervour with which you accepted those duties, one could be excused for thinking your talents might lay in that direction rather than towards the office, of course.'

Raina crimsoned, and berated herself roundly for having permitted him to provoke her into resurrecting what she most wanted forgotten. 'Then one couldn't be more wrong!' she pushed out with a reasonably scornful half laugh. 'Because I would've said it all depended on their relative attractions!'

'You could have a point there,' he conceded, the gleam in his eyes becoming chilled as they raked over her in an insolently deprecating appraisal. 'And that being the case, I'm sure you'll understand when I say I've suddenly remembered I wanted to see one of the men about something.' And with a slight tug on the brim of his hat in a caustic salute he about-turned and went striding back towards the yards.

Raina watched his progress for a few minutes with her head set at an uncaring angle, but with her lip caught doubtfully between even white teeth. She was pleased to have got her message across, naturally, but she was finding the manner and depth in which she had evidently succeeded in doing so not nearly so comforting. A totally estranged Dev was neither something she had wanted, nor something she was able to persuade herself she could handle. As she had noted before, her husband wasn't a man to be trifled with, and the thought of being in direct confrontation with him didn't exactly fill her with confidence, although there was no sign of any such apprehension in her demeanour when she continued on her way to the house.

Due to a purposely early use of the bathroom, Raina didn't see Dev again until they met in the billiard room before dinner, the presence of Ann, Joe, and Bevan, making it somewhat easier for her to act with a pseudo-naturalness. When he arrived, Dev carried with him a number of small notes which he immediately handed to Raina.

'More congratulations from friends and neighbours that have just come in over the radio,' he advised in ironic tones that, thankfully, only she seemed to detect, as he poured himself a drink. 'Did you see the others that were received this morning?'

'Yes, Ann passed them on to me,' she relayed with a tight little smile before reading the new messages. As previously, the names were mostly unfamiliar to her, but the sincerity in their good wishes was obvious, as was the fact that her husband was held in high standing by the far-flung community. 'It's very kind and thoughtful of them all. I suppose they heard about our marriage when you sent our wires this morning.'

'Oh, yes!' It was Ann who answered with a laugh. 'There's no hope of keeping anything like that a secret in the bush. Or anything else either, for that matter,' she added meaningfully. 'You know who's sick, who's pregnant, and who's buying what from where and for how much as soon as the people concerned do.'

Which meant, of course, that everyone would also know precisely what was said in the replies to her own telegrams, thought Raina ruefully. She didn't doubt they would generate wired returns—the speediest way to let their thoughts be known—and for the most part probably more concerned with offering recriminations rather than congratulations! She could only hope her relatives realised their replies would be heard by one and all and restrained their remarks accordingly, otherwise there was very likely to be some extremely interested, not to say embarrassing, speculation created!

As a result of her musings, telegrams and families remained in Raina's mind throughout the meal that followed, and not only her own but Dev's as well. After all, since he had said he was a partner in a family company, she presumed he'd had relatives to advise of their marriage too, even though he had never mentioned any of them specifically, so when he did offer to explain the workings of the office to her after dinner, albeit in markedly sardonic terms, her curiosity eventually got the better of her once they were alone.

'Did you also wire your family this morning about our—umm—marriage?' she therefore ventured to enquire.

'Of course.' His affirmation was clipped out with a touch of impatience, as if he considered such a question to have been unnecessary.

Raina hunched away from the shortness in his tone

deprecatingly, but pressed on notwithstanding. 'And—and will they be upset that you didn't tell them beforehand?'

'I doubt it.' His firmly shaped mouth suddenly began to twitch as if at some private joke. 'My parents are probably used to it by now.'

So his mother and father were still living, were they? Then with a somewhat confused frown pulling her winged brows together, 'Meaning, you've been married before?' He'd certainly never mentioned anything of the kind.

'Uh-uh!' he squashed that assumption in not particularly complimentary accents. 'Meaning, neither of my brothers, nor my sister, gave any warning when they were about to be married either. I guess it must be a family trait.'

'I see,' Raina nodded, feeling strangely relieved. She didn't know why, but somehow she hadn't liked the idea of him having been married before. Perhaps because the thought of being compared to a predecessor, and undoubtedly coming second in any such comparison due to the circumstances surrounding their marriage and the present state of tension that existed between them, she found a little disturbing. 'So how many brothers do you have?'

'Just two,' he revealed absently as he viewed her attempts at sorting the papers on his desk.

'And your parents? They're still on the land as well?'

He didn't look up, but merely nodded. 'Uh-huh. They live on the home property together with my sister and her husband, who do most of the managing of it these days.' Suddenly his eyes did lift to hers, consideringly. 'What makes you ask?'

He made it sound as if she was prying, and knowing she had unaccountably been more than casually interested, she coloured under his unswerving regard

and spread her hands in a slightly distracted gesture.
'I—well—if our marriage was a—a normal one as it's
supposed to be, it is only natural that I'd know
something about your family, isn't it?' she stammered.

'Except our *marriage* isn't remotely like a normal
one, is it, sweetheart?' he countered in a caustically
emphasised drawl.

'I said, "as—as it's supposed to be".' Her reminder
was defensively, tautly, voiced.

Dev muttered something savagely, though inaudibly,
beneath his breath, and then exhaled heavily. 'Okay,
what was it you wanted to know about in here?' he
returned to their reason for being in the office on a
brusque note.

Glad to be back on less controversial ground, Raina
swiftly moved to indicate the various piles of papers she
had left on the desk. 'Well, mainly, how you deal with
everything. For example, these papers and magazines.
Do you keep them, or—or what?'

He gave a negligent shrug. 'If there's something of
particular interest I might tear it out and keep it, but
usually there's so many of them that after they're read I
just file them ... like so.' He picked up the whole
bundle in question and dropped them into the
wastepaper basket. 'Now, what else?'

Momentarily, she was too busy trying not to smile to
reply. That was certainly one way of reducing it all to a
more manageable size. 'The letters asking for donations
and subscriptions,' she supplied at length.

Within a matter of seconds Dev had made two
separate piles, marking one such accumulation with
varying amounts where relevant. The others also found
their way into the wastepaper basket. 'Next?' he probed
laconically.

'Invoices,' she answered just as briefly.

'Paid at the end of each month. There's two cheque

books in the right hand drawer of the desk. They're also each for a different account so you'd better check with me again later to find out what each one covers before you start writing any cheques.' He paused, his lips taking on a sceptical slant. 'If you intend to continue with this, I guess we'll have to see about having your signature recorded at the bank too and then you'll be able to sign them as well.'

Raina's eyes flashed resentfully. *If* she intended to continue with it! Hadn't she proved that with the interest she'd displayed already? Not to mention her complaints about *not* having anything to do all day!

'Oh, I wouldn't want you to rush into anything! Why not just put me on a trial for six months?' she couldn't help but gibe. 'That should give you at least a glimmer of an idea as to my perseverence, shouldn't it?'

'Except that I'm aware of that already ... when you care to apply it!' Dev's swift retort was no less sarcastically made.

'Well, then?' she dared to demand, knowing full well just what he was alluding to, but determined not to drop her defiant gaze before his all the same.

'Let's just say, I suggest we conclude this conversation right now, or else you're likely to discover just how tenacious *I* can be as well ... when I put my mind to it!' he warned significantly.

A trait Raina had already sensed he possessed in full measure, and therefore decided, albeit grudgingly, it probably would be prudent to comply with his suggestion. 'All right, then if you're apparently so proficient at disposing of all this paperwork, how come there was so much of it laying around?' she questioned in a tone that still carried a hint of indignation rather than conciliation.

'Because since we don't have a daily mail service, when it does come it comes in bulk, and that lot didn't arrive until the day before Hayes's funeral.' He paused, his expression setting into mocking lines. 'Since when, as you might recall, I haven't exactly had much time to devote to it.'

She shrugged a bare acknowledgment, refusing to give him the satisfaction of rising to his taunting, and concentrated her attention instead on his mention of her father which returned to mind something that had puzzled her previously. 'So why take on more work by despatching those telegrams advising of his death, as well as apparently arranging the funeral, then? Surely that was Charley's responsibility, not yours!' A hint of asperity made itself noticeable.

'Save that, as the heat makes it somewhat imperative that funerals be conducted without delay, and in order to ensure everyone was notified in time, I merely deputised for him because he happened to have been out of town, and contact, on that particular day,' she was informed on a satiric note.

'I—I didn't realise,' she faltered uncomfortably, supposing that by rights she really owed him her thanks for having done what he did instead of her resentment.

'Another instance among many, evidently.' His goading surfaced as an expressive gibe.

Raina drew a sharp intake of breath, her blue eyes snapping. 'The worst of which was being unaware just how insufferable you can be!' she sniped spontaneously in turn and stormed from the room. It seemed the wisest course to take if their relationship wasn't to deteriorate any further because there was no way she was going to be circumspect with her remarks if he didn't also intend to do the same. And especially when all she had wanted to do was to discover some ways in which to keep herself occupied, and simultaneously help if possible!

Upstairs once again, she found she was in too volatile a frame of mind to even consider retiring for the night, however, and so, lighting a hopefully relaxing cigarette, she took a seat on the balcony and tried to reason herself into a calmer state.

Never had she met anyone who could make her lose control of both her temper and her composure quite so swiftly, or so effortlessly, and the knowledge perturbed her not a little. It put her at a distinct disadvantage— something else she had never before experienced—and where Dev Masters was concerned she would doubly have preferred it otherwise. Of course, it was probably only because the recent changes in her life had occurred so suddenly and she was still unaccustomed to the totally different environment, she justified encouragingly, whereas once she became more familiar with her surroundings and lifestyle on an outback station then doubtless Dev would be unable to put her off balance with such disconcerting ease too.

Comforted by the thought, and with her confidence considerably restored as a result, Raina stubbed out the remains of her cigarette and returned to her room. Noting as she did so the light shining from her husband's room next door. Filled as she was with renewed resolve, it gave her an idea and with due deliberation she proceeded to first lock the door that led into the passageway and then, with a definite and reassuring click, the lighter one connecting the two rooms. There! She dusted her hands together with satisfaction. That should convince him of her feelings, if nothing else, and for a bathroom he could avail himself of the main one down the hall!

With a congratulatory smile on her face she turned to begin undressing, but only to whip around again in shock and consternation scant seconds later when, presumably with the aid of a foot, the connecting door abruptly burst open with a violent force that had it swinging back against the wall with a resounding crash. Dev promptly strode through the opening, his expression thunderous, and had grasped hold of her shoulders in a rough grip before she even had time to recover.

'There'll be no bloody doors locked in this house, Raina!' he grated savagely before his mouth clamped down on hers in hard and punishing domination. 'Understand?'

She gulped convulsively, her eyes wide and apprehensive as she attempted to strain away from him, and uncertain just what he intended.

On seeing her wary look, Dev uttered a sardonic half laugh and without waiting for an answer swept her off her feet and tossed her carelessly on to the bed. 'Oh, don't worry, you can keep your chaste bed. I've no desire to share it with you!' he jeered down at her, his hands resting on lean hips. Then pacing back to the doorway with the same purposeful steps with which he had entered the room, he halted and fixed her with an implacable stare. 'But make no mistake, I meant what I said, sweetheart! I'll have no locked doors in this house just because you've suddenly decided to renege on your part of the bargain! For if you're ever tempted to try the same again, sparks will really fly, believe me!' Accomplished by an explicitly accentuating nod before he continued on into the other room.

Dropping her legs over the side of the bed, Raina remained sitting, but lifted a hand absently to touch lips that could still feel the forceful imprint of his. Shaken by the alacrity and fierceness of his retaliation she undoubtedly was, but at the same time she was also dismayingly conscious that amid the relief produced by his announcement regarding his lack of desire to share her bed there was a touch of inexplicable pique that he could dismiss her with such evident indifference!

Not that she *wanted* him to show any interest in her in that way, of course, otherwise she wouldn't have locked the door in the first place, she defended hastily. Nonetheless, despite her attempted explanations the feeling remained, and the fact that it did was sufficient to have her ire rising against herself for being so perverse and it was in a mood of extreme self dissatisfaction that she eventually finished making ready for bed.

Within three days both Raina and Dev had received their full complement of family telegrams in reply to the notifications of their marriage, although the response from the two sets of relatives came in totally different forms.

Dev's, on the one hand, simply expressed their congratulations and best wishes for the future and hoped it wouldn't be too long before they could actually meet his bride. On the other hand, however, those from Raina's family—apart from Malcolm whose felicitations she knew to be genuine, and her mother and stepfather whose congratulations were tempered by disappointment at neither having been advised beforehand nor invited to attend the ceremony—were of a considerably more rancorous and incensed nature than an approving or rejoicing one. Faith and Steven even going so far as to declare in theirs that they hoped she *didn't* expect them to offer their best wishes! A statement that, no doubt, created quite some interest among the other listeners when it was relayed over the radio, surmised Raina ruefully. Apparently her relations *hadn't* realised—or cared—that she wouldn't be the only one to learn of their unconcealed displeasure.

Dev's reaction to their not entirely unanticipated

acrimony was to shrug it off dispassionately, and taking her cue from him Raina did the same. What was done was done, and since she was still of the opinion that she was right to have prevented the whole of the estate from being liquidated, she saw no reason why she should allow her family to make her feel guilty merely because their extravagant schemes for the assets accrued from such a disposal had been frustrated.

At least, that was how she had begun to reassuringly view the situation, until only another two days later when, without any prior warning whatsoever, her cousin Adele suddenly arrived. Raina was in the stores shed at the time making out the station's half-yearly inventory of supplies. Another task she had willingly relieved Dev of doing and which she found most informative as well as enjoyable. But like everyone else around the homestead the sound of an unexpected plane coming in to land had her wandering to the door and looking towards the airstrip curiously as she wondered who it might be.

Without requiring any instructions, one of the men had already made his way across the intervening ground in one of the property's utilities to meet the aircraft's arrival, but as it was impossible to see the strip clearly from the stores shed Raina had had to wait for the vehicle's return to discover the reason for the plane's visit.

That it should have been Adele sitting next to the driver had her immediately executing a grimace of wry resignation. Unfortunately, it was all too easy to guess what had prompted her cousin's return! The sound of revving engines coming from the airstrip advised that the Cessna was about to depart and Raina sighed, knowing it signalled Adele wasn't intending for her visit to be a brief one.

'Is that really the best vehicle you can send to pick up

guests? It's obviously only a work vehicle and I must say I expected something better!' the older girl complained promptly on alighting. She proceeded to brush at her expensively designed outfit as if expecting it to have been covered in dirt, and then peered into the back of the ute. 'I hope my luggage hasn't been damaged either being thrown around in there.'

Noting the three matching red leather cases Raina's heart sank a little more. Clearly Adele's visit wasn't only not going to be a short one, it was going to be quite an extended one! 'Oh, I shouldn't think so,' she consoled with a valiantly pleasant smile. 'And I'm sorry you objected to the ute. Had we known you were coming, of course, we could have sent the station wagon.'

Adele made a sound of unimpressed long-suffering and waved a hand towards the man still seated behind the wheel of the vehicle. 'You, there!' she caught his attention imperiously. 'Take my luggage up to the house, and this time treat it with a little more respect!'

'If you wouldn't mind, Fred,' added Raina in an effort to relieve her cousin's commands of some of their arrogance—Adele never believed in showing any courtesy, or even civility at times, to anyone she considered her social inferior—and with an acknowledging smile the man drove off in the direction of the homestead.

'You know why I'm here, of course,' stated Adele peremptorily as the two girls followed on foot for the short distance.

'I think I've a fair idea,' owned Raina on a dry note.

'That's good, because the rest of us decided I'm probably the best one to convince you to give up this ridiculous stand you're taking!'

'It's a little late for that, isn't it?' Raina couldn't help giving a whimsical half laugh. 'I *am* already married, after all.'

'And you think we don't know why?' her dark haired relative rounded on her with sudden vehemence. 'Believe me, it's something Steven means to check into very thoroughly! To ascertain whether your marrying for the sole purpose of depriving the other shareholders of their rights is legal under the terms of the estate, because we all know very well it certainly wasn't any love match!'

Not that it had been solely to deprive anyone of their so-called rights, anyway, strictly speaking, but their reaction was precisely as Dev had predicted. Swallowing nervously, Raina forced a pseudo-confident smile on to her lips and countered, 'Wasn't it?'

Adele simply uttered a scoffing laugh. 'Oh, of course it wasn't! How could it be in such a short time, and especially when he paid you no attention whatever when we were all here?' Halting, she smiled somewhat smugly. 'As you may remember, *I* was the one all his interest was directed towards.'

Or vice versa, amended Raina sardonically to herself. Aloud, she merely saw fit to propose meaningfully, 'Then maybe I just caught him on the rebound when your return interest abruptly shrivelled on believing him to only be the manager of Ajax Downs.'

'You mean, he is actually more than that, then?' was her cousin's sharp retort.

'I guess you could say that, seeing it's his family's company that owns the station,' Raina conceded, shrugging.

'Well, well.' A secretive smile edged its way across Adele's face. 'That's something handy to know, isn't it?'

'Meaning?' Raina glanced at her apprehensively, beginning to suspect she could have done herself a disservice by divulging that singular piece of information.

'Oh, nothing in particular,' her cousin contended, but with such a pleased expression that Raina promptly disbelieved her. 'However, to return to your comment that it's too late for anything to be altered because you're already married, there is such a thing as divorce, you know ... as I'm only too aware.' With another laugh.

'And why should I consider that?' It was Raina's turn to smile now, if a little tautly. 'I've only been married a week.'

'Because if you're not already, you'll be regretting it by the time a month's passed, I'll be bound!' Adele forecast testily. 'Oh, be sensible, Raina! This isn't the life for you! You're used to the bright lights, yachting trips, the social round! You don't fit in here, and in no time you'll doubtlessly be bored to tears and cavilling at the heat and the isolation ... just like your mother before you!' She paused, her tone becoming infused with understanding. False and condescending understanding, to Raina's ears. 'All right, perhaps we were a little thoughtless to expect you to agree to the sale of the Estate so soon after your father's death, and we can even appreciate that Alliance may have slightly more meaning to you than the rest of the family, but for goodness sake don't take it to extremes by obstinately refusing to see the facts as they really are! I mean to say, is it really all worth this spurious marriage of yours?'

'Except that I—we,' Raina corrected quickly, protectively, her chin lifting to a defiant level, 'don't happen to consider it spurious! And if I hadn't considered it worth it, I wouldn't have married in the first place.'

'You're saying, Dev's of exactly the same opinion as you?' Adele's eyes narrowed itently.

The fact that there was still an air of tension between them made it difficult to maintain otherwise, particularly when she kept wondering herself whether he was already regretting their arrangement, but Raina still did her utmost to appear unflustered by the question by exclaiming with as much conviction as possible, 'Well, naturally!'

'I see,' Adele mused more than acknowledged as they mounted the front steps. 'So just where is he at the moment ... inside?' Looking expectantly towards the house.

Before Raina could answer Ann made an appearance and, asking for tea to be served on the verandah, the younger girl waited until the housekeeper had departed again before taking a seat opposite her cousin at the white lace table and replying. 'No, as a matter of fact he's over at Alliance today checking on some matters with Daniel. He is due to return before dinner, though.'

'But you, despite assertions to the contrary, were apparently neither eager enough to keep him company, nor to visit the property you profess means so much to you!' retorted Adele with pointed irony.

'Not at all,' Raina managed to deny after only a moment's discomfited hesitation. 'As it happens, this is his second trip in almost as many days, but as I accompanied him on the first one I simply decided to give it a miss on this occasion. When all's said and done, there are things for me also to attend to here, you realise.'

'And during a time when most newly weds would be on their honeymoon too!'

'It's not always possible for a grazier to take an extended leave of absence,' Raina parried, hoping against hope that Dev would say something similar if the subject was raised again in his presence. 'We'll probably fit one in some time before the end of the year, however.'

And so it continued for the remainder of the afternoon. Adele alternately probing, trying to catch her younger cousin out somewhere, or attempting to cajole her into agreeing to change her stand, while Raina evaded and prevaricated until she began to doubt her ability to remember everything she'd said.

Eventually, it was Dev's return that afforded her a respite, although on first seeing him approaching the homestead her worries increased for fear that he might inadvertently give the lie to something she had already said. Or more disastrous still, in view of how matters were between them at the moment, not even feel inclined to give his help at all. So it was with rather bated breath that she watched as he pushed open the screen door at the top of the verandah steps.

'Adele! This is a pleasant surprise,' he immediately greeted their visitor with an easy smile as he removed his hat and ran his fingers through his hair, ruffling it, on moving towards the table. Actually, he didn't appear surprised in the slightest to discover the older girl ensconced on his porch, noted Raina, and deduced that he had fortunately already been forewarned by someone else of their guest's arrival. 'If you'd let us know you were coming I could have ensured I was here to meet you too.' Momentarily, his eyes met Raina's significantly as he hung his headgear on its usual hook.

'Oh, that's all right,' Adele discounted airily. 'Raina and I have been having a nice talk anyway.' Hesitating, she sent him a somewhat arch look. 'You don't mind my visiting you unannounced ... and so soon after your marriage, I hope.'

'Of course not. Any members of either of our families will always be most welcome, won't they, kitten?'

Looking up to reply, Raina suddenly found him

bending over her, a hand coming to rest against the nape of her neck and tilting her face up to receive his lowering lips. Their contact with her own paralysed her for a moment, not only because it was so unexpected but also because his mouth moved on hers with a leisurely thoroughness that elicited an involuntary, but distinct response. When Dev lifted his head again their eyes connected briefly, and Raina was initially disconcerted and then furious to see the glint of provoking laughter that shone in his. That she could exhibit neither emotion in front of Adele was obvious, and knowing it had been purely for that girl's benefit had Raina flushing and averting her gaze vexedly.

'Sorry about that,' Dev apologised nonchalantly to Adele as he perched himself on the arm of Raina's chair and dropped a bronzed arm across her shoulders. 'But when you're newly married and you've been apart all day . . .' He gave an implicit half smile.

'How—however, to answer that last question,' Raina inserted unsteadily, the feel of her husband's hard, muscular thigh pressed against her arm doing little to aid her in regaining her composure, but determined to re-direct their attention regardless. 'Naturally I endorse Dev's views with regard to visitors. We're only too pleased to see them no matter when they come.'

'And after me replying with such a waspish telegram on hearing about your marriage too,' Adele sighed with dubious contrition. 'Can you ever forgive me?' With a wistful smile that was focused entirely on Dev.

Raina stiffened, knowing of old that when her cousin purposely set out to be charmingly humble she was at her most dangerous, but Dev merely flexed a wide shoulder and countered tolerantly, 'What's to forgive? Under the circumstances it's quite understandable that you should have been disappointed, and I doubt there's anyone who hasn't later regretted something they've said or done at a time of stress.'

Except for Adele, that was! qualified Raina worriedly. So just what was she up to now that she suddenly appeared as if butter wouldn't melt in her mouth? Whatever the reason, she flatly refused to believe it was due to any change of heart concerning her cousin's desires, and she said as much to Dev later when they were dressing for dinner.

'Oh, I don't know,' he shrugged impassively in response as he passed through her room from the bathroom to his own, his voice reverting to its more recent clipped accents. Then slanting her a mocking glance over a bare shoulder, 'Perhaps our—er—loving display was sufficiently convincing to have her changing her opinion.'

If not completely unperturbed by the sight of his half naked form passing to and fro through her room any more, then at least gradually becoming accustomed to it, Raina refused to be distracted and, ignoring his taunting look, hurried to the connecting door after him. 'Since it was evident nothing I said this afternoon was sufficient to convince her, then it's going to take a lot more than one kiss to succeed!' she scoffed.

'So what are you suggesting? That we make love in full view of her, in the hope that will?' His brows rose to a goading peak.

'Hardly!' she grimaced gibingly, reddening slightly. 'I just meant, she isn't that easily swayed from her purpose, and the time to be wariest of Adele is when she's at her sweetest!'

'A typical woman, in other words!'

'You can call it a typical whatever you like!' Raina fired back, nettled. 'Just don't underestimate her, that's all!'

'Not like I did you, huh?'

There was a sting in his voice that had her heart missing a beat and her eyes shading guardedly. 'H-how do you mean?'

'I mean, you expect others to keep to their part of a bargain even though you chicken out of yours, don't you, sweetheart?' he bit out. 'So maybe it's time for me to ask just what my participation in this is worth to you!'

Raina felt her stomach contract and she dropped her gaze selfconsciously, knowing their arrangement *had* been one-sided so far. 'You're making th-that a condition for you helping me?' she hazarded throatily, not pretending to be unaware of just what part of their deal he was accusing her of evading.

A muscle corded beneath Dev's tanned cheek as he stared at her for a long unnerving second, and then he let out an irritated sigh, dragging a hand roughly around the back of his neck. 'No, I'm not making that a condition!' he rasped. 'I was simply wondering if you're prepared to do *anything* in order to retain Alliance, because to date you sure haven't contributed much to the damned arrangement! So far it all seems very similar to your normal method of operation ... you get the advantages while someone else does all the work!'

'That's not fair!' she felt justified in protesting. 'I've tried to do my share by relieving you of what office work I can.'

'Oh, ripper!' he lauded caustically. 'And especially since the office work's never caused me any problems!'

'But our sleeping together *would* make less work for you?' she sniped, her eyes widening facetiously.

'No, but we would then have a proper marriage at least ... and that could make it rather more worthwhile than it is at present!'

'But you said only the other night that you had no

wish to share my bed!' she abruptly recalled, not a little triumphantly.

'And nor do I until you finally own that you *also* have obligations to fulfil—as you agreed to—and can do so willingly,' he advised in stony accents.

Uncomfortably aware that she had made such an agreement, Raina shifted restively. 'Then knowing I was only interested in a business arrangement in the first place, I'm beginning to wonder why you agreed to marry me at all!' she flared, taking out her feelings of guilt on him.

Dev's eyes raked her with a deprecating gaze. 'A question I've asked myself a number of times during the last week!' he retorted squashingly.

Oddly, once again Raina found his cold rebuff had the power to hurt and she pressed her lips together to stop their sudden trembling. 'And—and while Adele's here?' she faltered, prudently taking the opportunity to revert to their original topic.

His mouth took on a cynical upturn. 'Oh, don't get into a sweat, I'll keep to my part of the bargain! One of us has to, don't they?'

There didn't seem anything she could say in reply to that and so, with a disconsolate sigh, she turned and moved back into her own room, her thoughts a confused and bewildered jumble. She just couldn't understand why, when she wasn't prepared to sleep with him, his rejections of her should produce the painful feelings they did instead of the relief she would have expected. Oh, God, just what on earth *did* she want? she despaired.

CHAPTER SEVEN

DURING the following week, however, Raina had no such difficulty in ascertaining just what her cousin Adele wanted, because it very quickly became abundantly plain that that girl's sights were set squarely on the boss of Ajax Downs. Whether it was purely in an attempt to somehow prove Raina and Dev's marriage wasn't all it appeared, or simply because her own interest in him had been rekindled on learning he wasn't merely the manager of the property, Raina couldn't decide—after all, Dev had seemed quite willing to show Adele some attention before, and if she couldn't force her cousin into divorcing him, there was always the chance she could achieve the same desired result by inciting him to divorce her!—but the fact that her husband always indulgently agreed to the older girl accompanying him almost wherever he went, she found both worrying and infuriating.

Granted, there was nothing specific in his behaviour towards herself that she could complain about, although he had certainly never kissed her again in Adele's presence in the way he had the day she arrived—he had never kissed her again at all, in fact, she noted—but at the same time it was for Adele that he reserved his most relaxed attitude, and his laughter, while towards Raina he was simply sufficiently polite in the company of others, though somewhat unapproachable when they were alone. But except for the first morning he hadn't even bothered to enquire if she would care to join them! she remembered with some asperity.

It had happened at breakfast, a meal Dev usually shared with Joe and Bevan at a much earlier hour, but presumably in deference to their visitor he had joined Raina and Adele at the table that particular morning.

'I've been looking forward to doing some riding while I'm here if it's possible,' Adele had opened the conversation brightly, looking at Dev. Adding with a captivating smile, 'And if you'll join me as my guide.'

'It will be my pleasure,' he had agreed unhesitatingly with a smooth inclination of his head.

'Starting today?' Adele had promptly quizzed with evident pleasure.

'I don't see why not.'

'Oh, lovely! It's ages since I've been on a horse,' had beamed Adele, while across from her Raina had grimaced sardonically. All of a sudden it appeared her husband's extra work was able to take second place!

'And you, Raina, do you feel like coming too?' he had suddenly turned to ask of her. Albeit not particularly enthusiastically, she had noticed.

Caught offguard—he'd never so much as hinted that she could accompany him before!—and strangely loath to confess that she couldn't ride anyway, she had hunched a slender shoulder and begun flusteredly, 'I—umm—well . . .'

'Oh, Raina doesn't ride,' Adele had had no compunction in cutting in to reveal with a laugh. 'In fact, I don't think she's ever even been *on* a horse.'

Dev had merely raised one brow fractionally at the disclosure, his gaze remaining fixed on his wife. 'I'd have thought you'd belong to the polo set,' he'd commented drily.

'Oh, she does.' It had been Adele who was free with the information again. 'Although only in the capacity of a spectator, of course, *I'm* the rider in the family.'

'So it would appear,' Dev had smiled at her before

turning back to Raina to advise, 'If you'd like to learn, though, I'll get Bevan to teach you.'

He wasn't interested in doing it himself obviously! It had been enough to have her tilting her chin defensively higher. 'No, thank you,' she had declined with a touch of disdain. 'It's never particularly interested me and, to be quite honest, I prefer driving racy sports cars, actually.' The last had been added in retaliation, even if it was something of an exaggeration.

Dev had merely given an indifferent shrug and the subject had been dropped, but as the days passed Raina would often find herself stopping what she was doing and covertly watching them as they set off across the plains, and then spend the ensuing few minutes speculating as to just why she, herself, hadn't even learnt to ride.

She thought she could remember having wanted to at one time many, many years ago, but that she hadn't been allowed—her mother having had something against it for some reason, she presumed—and since then she supposed it had just become one of those things she had never got around to doing.

Now, however, and in spite of her claimed lack of interest, she was becoming more and more aware of a feeling that was almost akin to envy as she watched them mount up every day. There was something that attracted her just in the manner in which Dev, especially, swung into the saddle—an easy grace that somehow seemed to convey an underlying capable strength at the same time, and doubtlessly acquired from having spent a lifetime on horseback—and which eventually had her resolving that she was going to learn to ride, whether he was uninterested in teaching her or not! And not only that, but come hell or high water, she was going to do it better than Adele!

Her decision made, Raina wasted no time in

procuring for herself a pair of short-sided stock boots and a bush hat from the stores shed to go with her own jeans and shirt, her clothes having thankfully arrived a day or two before, and then it was merely a matter of arranging confidentially with Bevan—since Dev had apparently considered it too much of a chore for himself to undertake, she saw no reason for him to be advised at all—a convenient time for her lessons to begin. Bevan, at least, making it obvious that he didn't find the prospect onerous in the slightest!

Due to Raina's desire for secrecy it was decided that the best time would be when Dev and Adele left on their daily, early morning rides, and so, no sooner had the dust settled after their departure the following day than she joined the jackaroo at the saddle shed.

'Hey, Brian!' Bevan immediately shouted to one of the stockmen who happened to be passing. 'Get Duchess out of the yard and saddle her up for the Missus. Be quick about it too, we don't want to be waiting here all day!' He turned to Raina with a disgruntled grimace as the man set off for the yard. 'You have to be on their backs all the time or else half of these fellers wouldn't bestir themselves enough to get out of their own way! Dev's much too lenient with them and they take advantage of the fact. Hell, he even lets *everyone* on the property call him by his first name, instead of which he should be making them call him "boss" as a continual reminder of just who's in charge!'

From what she had seen, Raina had never doubted for one minute that her husband wasn't always in full control. 'But they often do call him that, anyway,' she put forward with a slight frown. This was a new side she was witnessing of the normally easy-going young man she knew from the homestead.

'Oh, sure!' His agreement was sardonically made.

'But only in a familiar way, not with the subservience it should be said.'

The furrows creasing Raina's forehead deepened fractionally. 'I don't think he *wants* his staff, or anyone else on the station if it comes to that, to feel servile.'

'Exactly! And because they don't, they turn it to their own account by slacking at every opportunity!'

Admittedly her experience was limited, but she certainly hadn't seen any such signs. And besides ... 'I've never heard Dev make any such complaint. In fact, just the opposite, most times.'

'Because he's too tolerant with them, as I said! Believe me, they know who's in command when I give the orders, though!'

A statement she was swiftly, but not altogether favourably, coming to believe! In any event, she also preferred to be on friendly rather than remote terms with the station's residents, and therefore went out of her way to show her appreciation when the fair haired stockman returned to the saddle shed leading a dark brown mare. As well, determining that if she was going to learn to ride she would start with the basics, she saved him the trouble of saddling the horse by advising she would do so herself.

'Okay, I'll be on my way, then,' Ed smiled in return. Pausing, he added helpfully, 'She's a nice quiet mount, so you shouldn't have much trouble with her if you're not used to riding, Raina.'

'Mrs Masters, to you, Dymock!' instructed Bevan peremptorily. 'And when we want your opinion we'll ask for it! Now I might suggest you ...'

'Just one moment, thank you, Bevan,' Raina cut in on him somewhat summarily herself, liking his attitude less and less, and wondering incidentally if her husband was aware of the fashion in which his jackaroo spoke to his employees. 'I believe it's *my* prerogative to decide as to just how I shall be addressed, and as I've already given permission for my christian name to be used, that's how I wish it to continue! Moreover, I appreciated Brian's comments!' She gave the stockman an eloquent smile, guessing he must have surmised that, if not a beginner then she at least wasn't a particularly experienced rider, due to her never having taken a horse out before.

Beneath his tan a dark flush—part anger, part embarrassment—stained Bevan's face and, noting it, Raina supposed she really shouldn't have taken him to task in front of one of the staff even though she considered he deserved it for having no reservations about doing the same to someone else—quite apart from his having had the temerity to assume it was his right to tell anyone what they might or might not call her. However, once Brian had prudently taken his leave—although not without a rather gratified look on his face, she noticed ruefully—she sent the younger man beside her a conciliatory glance.

'I'm sorry for sounding off at you in front of him like that, Bevan, but I had already given him leave to call me by my first name,' she explained in apologetic tones.

'Apparently,' he conceded stiffly, his expression as black as it had been in the billiard room on the night when Joe's bantering had displeased him. 'However, it won't do much for my command over the men if you intend to veto my every order to them in future!'

'Oh, of course I don't!' she protested with a sigh. He was tending to blow the whole episode out of proportion. 'I only did it this time because I was involved. On any other occasion, I doubt I'd know which orders to override, in any case . . . even if I did have the authority to do so.' Something she strongly suspected Dev would neither appreciate, nor approve her assuming! 'Nevertheless, if you now feel you'd rather not go ahead with teaching me to ride ...' She spread her hands meaningfully, concealing her disappointment at the probability, but feeling obliged to give him the opportunity to back out all the same.

Bevan shrugged. 'No, I said I would, and I will,' he declared, his manner easing a little.

Pleased, as well as thankful, Raina tried to put the unfortunate incident behind them as quickly as possible by promptly half turning towards the shed and enquiring animatedly, 'So what do I need first ... a saddle?'

'I rather think Duchess would prefer a blanket before one of those,' he amended wryly, noticeably relaxing even more. Opening the door of the shed, he motioned for her to enter with him. 'Come on, I'll show you everything you need.'

With a rueful smile for her mistake, Raina followed him inside interestedly. She had been through the building before on her explorations the day after her marriage, but at the time her attention to the contents had been only cursory. Now, as Bevan began to point out all the various pieces of equipment, she wondered if she would ever remember which was which and just what function they each served. And not only that, but it wasn't until he had sorted through all the saddles available looking for one suitable for her that she even realised they came in different sizes! Previously, she had just assumed a saddle was a saddle and everyone used the same, but she was abruptly coming to see there was more to riding than she had ever suspected.

Her gear eventually selected, Raina helped Bevan carry it all outside, the period of instruction that ensued proving to be not only informative but very pleasant as well as her companion regained his normal good humour, while she discovered she possessed a most satisfying, though totally unexpected, aptitude for the pursuit. In truth, she found it so agreeable that she was reluctant to bring the lesson to a halt, but knowing that Dev and Adele were likely to return at any minute finally had her grudgingly doing so, and thanking Bevan for his time and patience, she unsaddled the docile brown mare and returned her to the paddock, then hurried back to the homestead in order to change into a softly feminine cotton dress before going down to breakfast.

Trixie, one of the house girls, had only just served her with her grapefruit when Dev and Adele entered the dining room, both of them lookingly slightly wind-tousled but full of life and vigour. Momentarily, Raina felt a tug at her heart at the dynamic picture her husband presented, but suppressing it rapidly she forced a politely interested look on to her face as her gaze encompassed both of them.

'Did you have a nice ride?' she asked.

'Oh, marvellous!' It was Adele who answered vivaciously as she swept her hair into place with long fingers and took a seat across the table. 'We followed the river all the way to Ajax Gorge, which is really the most magical place. Isn't it, Dev?' She smiled—almost coyly, Raina thought, and felt her blood pressure start to rise as a result—in that man's direction as he too seated himself.

'It's certainly pretty,' he acceded on an indolent note. 'That's why I thought you might like to see it.'

'And so I did. The beautiful clear water, the magnificent colours in the rock walls, jewel-bright parrots and blue-winged kookaburras! We even saw a couple of jabiru storks wading around, and a not so active crocodile sunning itself on the bank,' enthused Adele spiritedly. 'You really ought to make an effort to go out there some time, Raina. Oh, but how silly of me, of course I was forgetting you don't ride,' added with extremely dubious dismay, 'and unless you feel like walking for absolutely *miles*, which I'm sure you don't, I doubt you'd be able to reach it any other way.'

'In that case, I guess I'll just have to give it a miss, then, won't I?' Raina acceded quite imperturbably. Because inwardly she was pleasurably making a note to visit the area as soon as her riding proficiency was equal to the journey. 'Or who knows, if Dev should happen to put in a road that way, it may not be quite so inaccessible in the years to come. After all, I've a whole lifetime in which to see it . . . haven't I?' Her pause was a significant one, her deep blue gaze slanting towards her husband meaningfully.

For an instant his own eyes remained locked watchfully with hers, his expression tightening imperceptibly, and then he hunched a denim-clad shoulder dispassionately. 'I suppose that's one way of figuring it,' he allowed.

Meaning, he didn't any more because he was finding Adele's company more to his liking than her own? she surmised with a sinking feeling and returned her attention to her grapefruit despondently. It appeared Adele could be getting closer to achieving her ends as each day passed.

Presently, Trixie put in her second appearance with another two grapefruit filled, cut glass bowls, but as he started on his own, Dev suddenly seemed to become aware that Raina was still only half way through hers and he cast her a partly surprised, partly quizzical glance.

'You're usually almost finished with breakfast by the time we arrive back from our rides. Didn't you rise until later this morning?'

Hugging her secret to herself, she gave a small shrug. 'There didn't appear any reason not to lay in for a while,' she lied. Adding in deliberately dejected tones, in the hope of making him experience a twinge of guilt for a change, 'And eating on one's own is hardly something to be anticipated with great eagerness, anyhow.'

Apparently she succeeded in her aim too for he immediately apologised, 'I'm sorry, I guess I just didn't realise.'

He might have done if he hadn't been so busy giving Adele all his attention! she flared silently.

'So why don't you come with us today, hmm?' he continued. 'We're mustering out at the Eight Mile Yards and you'll probably enjoy getting away from the homestead for a while.'

"Us" being Adele and himself! she presumed with some asperity. And he thought she would *enjoy* playing gooseberry around her own husband! 'Perhaps some other time . . . when your—er—work may not require so much of your attention,' she declined with acid inference. 'Besides, Ann's making bread today and I've promised to help her.'

'You . . . bake bread?' Adele interposed with a scornful laugh. 'That would be something to see! You've never shown any interest in such domestic activities before.'

'Mmm, but then, I've never before lived in an area where you can't just walk down the street and buy a loaf whenever you want one either!' Raina retorted pungently, deducing that it wasn't Adele's wanting her to accompany them that had caused her to decry the idea, but purely an excuse to be disdainfully patronising—as per usual!

The older girl widened her brown eyes expressively. 'So why should you concern yourself about that when you already have servants capable of doing it for you? I certainly don't remember you displaying any inclination to participate in kitchen duties when you were at home.'

'Probably because replacing cooks and housekeepers

in Perth is no great hassle compared to what it could be here, and for all anyone knows, there may come a time when I *have* to do it, and then what would we do if I didn't know how?'

'We could always buy in a supply from Wallaby Creek or Kununurra and freeze it if it really became necessary,' inserted Dev smoothly.

Undecided whether he was merely being helpful, or actually supporting her cousin, Raina flashed him a direful glare anyway. 'Then why don't we do that now?' she demanded.

'Mainly because everybody prefers home-made bread and Ann's quite amenable to making it.'

'But if I made it, you think everyone's preferences would abruptly alter, is that it?' she seethed. No matter what she tried to do he still refused to see her as anything but a useless socialite!

Dev uttered a muffled expletive. 'No, you . . .!'

'Goodness gracious!' broke in Adele, clicking her tongue slyly. 'Anyone would think you two hated rather than—umm—loved each other.'

Raina swallowed heavily in dismay, a visible smudge of colour stealing uncontrollably into her creamy skinned cheeks, but thankful for the timely reminder nonetheless. 'Y-yes . . . well . . . without the fighting one can't really appreciate the peace,' she just managed to push out with studied nonchalance. 'Isn't that so, my love?' Focussing pseudo limpid blue eyes in her husband's direction.

Dark brown eyes fastened mockingly to blue. 'Or, put another way, how can one hope to possess a kitten and escape being scratched,' he drawled.

The sarcastic louse! smouldered Raina, snatching her gaze away, although ensuring there was no evidence of any such vehemence in her expression as she smiled sweetly at her cousin and began rising to her feet. 'You see! How could I possibly *not* simply adore him when he's so overwhelmingly forebearing?' she cooed in falsely honeyed accents. But determined he was going to pay for the remark, she moved close to Dev's side. 'In fact, I find it so heart-warming that I'm afraid you'll just have to excuse me for wanting to reward him here and now.' She sent another smile, somewhat more taunting than apologetic actually, towards the other girl and, bending swiftly, placed a supposedly loving kiss to her husband's sun-bronzed cheek.

What she hadn't foreseen, however, was that Dev would just as quickly cup the back of her head on one of his hands, thereby enabling him to force her lips into burning contact with his own. It also permitted him to usurp the initiative as to when they should part again—and that wasn't for some considerable, wholly disquieting minutes! it seemed to Raina in her mounting agitation and fury at having the tables turned so perturbingly on her plan of revenge. When at last he did consent to set her free, her eyes were spitting fire and her breasts heaving rapidly with the force of her tumultuous feelings.

'Mmm, there is quite a lot to be said for making up after a fight, isn't there?' Dev mused provokingly before she could explode with the scorching words that were on the tip of her tongue.

Raina struggled for control, reminded once again of Adele's inquisitive presence, and eventually managed to produce a facsimile of a smile, albeit between somewhat gritted teeth. 'And especially when it means so much to *both* of us,' she stressed on a sweetly facetious note. 'But now,' with an expression of assumed regret, 'if you'll excuse me, I think I'll just have to leave you two to reminisce about your ride alone as Ann's probably waiting for me.' She started for the door without delay.

'You're not going to finish your breakfast?' called Dev after her in a whimsical drawl.

'I find I don't have much of an appetite this morning,' she threw back over her shoulder as she continued on her way without slowing.

Regardless of how flippant and uncaring an attitude she attempted to convey, however, Raina knew her inner feelings to be something else again. And as the days passed, and Adele continued to commandeer so much of Dev's time and attention, she gradually began to realise that somewhere along the line her apprehensions concerning her cousin's presence had changed from one of worry that the estate might yet be dissolved, to an even greater fear that she might lose her *husband*!

And why? For a time she refused to even contemplate a deeper reason than the rationalisation she kept fobbing herself off with that it was merely because he was her only hope of keeping the estate intact, but as her consternation and despair at the sight of them always together developed into an almost consuming anguish she was unable to delude herself any longer. She had fallen in love with her own husband! But too late, apparently, judging by his current interest in Adele!

Damn him, damn her, damn the pair of them! she railed helplessly. And damn herself too for having been so stupid as not to have known why her senses had always responded so willingly whenever he kissed her! Now it seemed she had lost whatever opportunities she may have had of arousing any reciprocal feelings within him. She could hardly just baldly announce that she had decided she would sleep with him after all, and knowing his emotions had never been involved anyhow, she just couldn't bring herself to try and compete with Adele in order to win him back to her side either when

it was extremely doubtful her efforts would be wanted
or even appreciated.

No, all she could really do was wait and hope that
her cousin would tire of her newest conquest in time, as
she had always done with others in the past, and in the
meantime keep herself busy, and thus her mind well
occupied with less demoralising thoughts.

To this end, Raina set about helping Ann however
she could; learning to re-stock their supplies by the
gross and the ton rather than by individual tins and
packets; and even overcoming her initial nervousness
with the housekeeper's help and joining in the "galah"
sessions, as they were called, held over the Flying
Doctor radio network every day for the purpose of
allowing those living in isolated areas to have contact
and a general talk with others of their kind.

Quite a few of the women she spoke to in this manner
Raina soon realised were among those she had met at
her father's funeral, and when one of them invited her
to their next monthly Women's Auxiliary meeting at a
neighbouring property she accepted with pleasure. Not
only in the hope of changing their estimation of her for
having ignored her father all those years, but also
because she looked forward to the chance to firmly
match faces to the voices she conversed with over the
radio and because she was finding she *wanted* to
become a part of the community that, notwithstanding
it being spread over many hundreds of square miles,
was obviously still a close-knit one.

Of course, she also utilised every possible moment
she could spare in improving her riding skills as well,
mostly under Bevan's instructions but, as she progressed, sometimes on her own. Actually, she gradually
came to prefer those times when he wasn't there for,
although he was helpful and patient, she still couldn't
help but dislike his manner towards the other men and,

worse, she had started to feel a trifle uncomfortable when alone in his company due to what appeared to be his slightly changed attitude towards herself.

The trouble was there was nothing openly objectionable in his manner for which she could legitimately rebuke him. It was just a series of incidents, like ... him always insisting on holding her about the waist to help give her a lift into the saddle even though she was quite capable of mounting without any assistance now; his hand continuing to rest on her thigh when she was seated on Duchess and he was standing beside her giving instructions; or the way he always seemed to brush against her when they were taking her gear to and from the saddle shed. Separately, she may not even have noticed them, she was prepared to admit, but together she was all too conscious of them, though reluctant to remark on them for fear of causing them both a deal of embarrassment should they, indeed, only have been unconscious rather than familiar actions.

Nevertheless, on most occasions now when she had to go into the shed, Raina tried to make sure Bevan was otherwise engaged outside before hurrying into its dim interior, but on one particular morning some two weeks or so after her lessons began, she was in the process of returning her saddle to its supporting pegs on the wall when she suddenly felt him close behind her and his two arms reached around to finish the task for her.

'You should have asked me to do that for you,' he lowered his head near to her ear to admonish softly. 'It's too heavy for someone like you.'

Caught between his surprisingly sturdy frame and the wall, Raina twisted around with difficulty to face him. 'Oh, I don't know. I've done it before,' she half laughed, doing her best to pass the matter off casually, and to surreptitiously extricate herself at the same time.

'In any event, a rider who couldn't even lift their own saddle would be a bit useless, don't you think?'

To her dismay, instead of putting more distance between them he leaned closer, his hands resting against the wall on either side of her head. 'What I think, is that you're lonely for some male attention . . . like this!' His arms abruptly caught her against him and his mouth swooped down on to hers harshly.

Wrenching her lips free, if not herself from his binding arms, Raina glared up at him in outrage. 'How dare you presume to do, or even think, any such thing!' she blazed. 'In case it's escaped your notice, I happen to have a husband to provide any male attention I might require!'

'Oh, don't give me that!' he discounted with something of a sneer. 'He spends more time with that cousin of yours than he does with you! And you think I don't know why you've been spending so much time with me! Why don't you just admit it's this you've been after? Believe me, I'm quite willing to oblige.' He sank a hand into her hair to immobilise her head as his mouth clamped voraciously over hers once more, his other hand seeking and finding a rounded breast.

Disgusted and enraged though she was by his assault, Raina at least now found her arms free and, grabbing for a halter from a nearby rail, she swung it with all her strength against the side of his head. Not unnaturally, Bevan gave a growl of pain and stepped back, putting a hand to his ear where a buckle had broken the skin.

'You bitch!' he immediately exploded wrathfully, his eyes glittering grimly on seeing the blood covering his fingers. 'You'll pay for . . .'

'No, *you're* the one who'll be paying, Bevan, if there's any paying to be done!' she broke in on him no less fiercely. 'Because I'm warning you, if you ever dare lay a hand on me again I'll kill you, so help me!'

'And if she doesn't, I bloody well will!'

The savagely ground out threat had them both looking to the doorway in surprise as Dev strode rapidly towards them, his mouth tight-lipped, his eyes slitted with a murderous gaze. Behind him, Adele remained at the entrance to the shed, looking on with avid and malicious interest.

'Roll your swag, Rawson!' The time-honoured bushman's form of dismissal was delivered by Dev in a stinging whiplash of sound that even had Raina wincing. 'You're finished on Ajax Downs, and with the Territory Pastoral Company, and if you know what's good for you, you'll be off this place before the hour's out!'

'Oh, and why should I?' Bevan countered with a rasp, evidently not about to accept the decision without a fight. *'She's* the one who's been wanting me to meet her secretly all this time!'

Dev's ebony framed eyes were as forbidding as his voice as they pinpointed his wife. 'It this true?'

'Well, yes,' Raina had no option but to concede, reluctantly. Then her voice strengthened. 'But not for the . . .'

'There! She admits it!' Bevan cut her off in victorious tones. 'So why should I be penalised just because she showed herself willing for a little extra-marital activity? And why should you care, anyway? It's more than obvious your interest lays elsewhere!'

It was a reckless comment to have made and the jackaroo would have to have been blind not to realise it on seeing the older man's jaw clench uncompromisingly. 'Except that she still does happen to be my *wife*! And willing, I think you said?' He glanced pointedly at the head-stall Raina was still clutching in her hand, and then the other man's bleeding ear. 'That's not exactly the impression I get . . . and nor did it *sound* it from what I heard!'

Bevan dropped his gaze for a moment, half shrugging discomfitedly. 'Yeah—well—maybe she's the type who—who just likes to lead a man on, or—or perhaps she saw you and put it all on for your benefit,' he charged in somewhat blustering accents.

'That's a lie!' protested Raina, her eyes lifting beseechingly to Dev's, desperate for him to believe her. 'I couldn't possibly have seen you, and nor did I lead him on either! He's simply saying that in an attempt to excuse his own contemptible actions!'

'And she's nothing but a teasing, lying . . .'

'That's enough, Rawson!' Dev interrupted him on a grating note. 'As I said, you've got one hour to leave this property so I don't suggest you waste any more of my time, or yours!'

'Huh!' the jackaroo jeered scornfully as he brushed past Dev. 'I should have known you'd take her lying word against mine! Not that I'll be sorry to see the last of this place, mind you! It'll be a pleasure to get back to a more tightly run station than this one!'

A few minutes of tense silence followed his rancorous departure during which Raina was all too aware of her husband's stony and unbending demeanour. 'I—I'm sorry,' she murmured shakily. 'B-but . . .'

'Are you all right?' he broke in on her to enquire peremptorily.

There wasn't the slightest sign of any softening in his voice and she nodded disconsolately. 'Yes, thank you.'

'Then I suggest we continue this in private up at the house!' He removed the head-stall from her suddenly nerveless fingers and tossed it cursorily over the rail, then catching hold of her upper arm in an impersonal grip began ushering her out of the shed.

So he hadn't altogether believed her after all, Raina despaired, and shivered involuntarily as she tried to keep up with his purposeful, long-legged stride.

For her part, dressed in pale fawn jodhpurs and a sky blue silk shirt, Adele looked as elegant and self-possessed as always as she joined them on Dev's other side. 'Well, that *was* an extraordinary prelude to breakfast,' she remarked with something of a smirk, although to no one in particular seemingly. 'It never ceases to amaze me what an earlier than expected return can uncover on occasion.'

Raina drew an angry breath at her cousin's patent effort to insinuate she had been a willing participant, but from the quelling look Adele received in response from Dev she was at least able to derive some satisfaction from seeing that girl forced into judiciously holding her tongue for a change, however grudgingly. It wasn't until they had crossed the verandah and entered the front door of the homestead that anyone spoke again. The first one to do so being Dev.

'We'll join you in the dining room for breakfast shortly,' he advised Adele summarily and, while that girl made off in the appropriate direction with a noticeable flounce, he urged Raina further along the hallway and into the office.

Closing the door behind them with a definite snap, Dev remained standing with his back to it, his hands coming to rest on lean hips as she moved further inside. 'Well?' he demanded curtly.

'Well, what?' She spun to face him resentfully. After all she had been through this morning, wasn't she even entitled to expect him to show at least *some* sympathy and concern?

'Well, had you been encouraging him?'

'Did I look as if I was from the condition of his ear?' she countered with undisguised sarcasm. 'Or are you now thinking it may have been the result of an over-enthusiastic love bite?'

'Right at the moment I'm thinking I'd like to throttle you!' he retaliated, the rasp of exasperation laced with icy anger in his tone.

'Well, don't let the fact that I've already had to suffer the unwanted mauling of one male this morning prevent you!' she gibed. 'Or perhaps you would even prefer it if *I* left and Bevan stayed! Would that suit you better?'

A muscle rippled along the line of Dev's jaw. 'Nothing doing, sweetheart!' he vetoed with an adamant, but sardonic, shake of his head. 'You made your bed, now you can lie in it! In any event, I haven't been particularly happy with his attitude towards the men for some time now.'

So he had known about it! His initial remark meaning, however, that she was just going to have to suffer everyone believing her guilty and therefore responsible for Bevan's unfair dismissal, she supposed. Her eyes locked bitterly with his.

'Well, thanks at least for your unqualified trust! It sure doesn't take much to have you thinking the worst of me, does it? But then . . .,' she paused, biting at an abruptly trembling lower lip, 'when haven't you?'

Dev gave a short bark of mirthless laughter. 'You call it *"not much"* when you openly admit you've been meeting him secretly! What the hell did you expect me to think on hearing that?'

'If you'd bothered to ask me instead of immediately assuming it automatically implied I was interested in him personally, I just may have expected you to believe the truth!'

'That being?'

Raina turned to stare unseeingly out of the window, strangely reluctant even now to actually reveal her secret. 'Ask any of the men, they'll be able to tell you,' she therefore parried with a shrug.

A forceful hand on her shoulder whirling her back to face him again was her first inclination that Dev had even moved. 'Except that it's *your* answer I want, not theirs!' he bit out.

'Why? Don't you trust them either?' she dared to snipe.

He uttered a fierce epithet and made to catch hold of her again, but momentarily the movement somehow reminded Raina of when Bevan had done much the same and she instinctively jumped backwards out of his reach, her eyes becoming wide and wary.

'All right, all right!' she choked defeatedly, her vision beginning to blur with sudden, unbidden tears. 'I asked him to teach me to ride! Just like you said I should if I wanted to learn!' Her swimming eyes connected explicitly with his.

For a moment he stared at her incredulously. 'And that's *all* it was?'

'Yes, that's *all* it was!' she confirmed on a slightly flaring note of resentment that he should apparently still have doubts.

'Oh, God!' Dev raked a hand through his hair savagely. 'I *will* kill the lousy bastard!' Breathing deeply, he sent her a frowning glance. 'But why secretly, for heaven's sake?'

Relieved though she was that he at last seemed to believe her, Raina now found herself beset by the problem of trying to explain her motives. Something she was even more loath to do. 'Oh, I don't know,' she shrugged diffidently as a result. 'I just wanted to—to surprise everyone, I guess.'

'Surprise . . . or show?' he put forward subtley, his lips taking on an oblique twist.

She flushed faintly, but stood her ground. 'I said,

surprise,' she insisted doggedly. As she recalled, the showing, had primarily been intended for her patronising cousin's benefit!

Thankfully he didn't pursue the point, but half smiled ruefully instead, 'Well, you've certainly managed that one way and another. Although what possibly amazes me most is none of the men mentioning it either, if as you say, they've also known what's been going on. Or did you get them to all swear a vow of secrecy too?'

'No!' she refuted huffily, surmising he was insinuating she had been encouraging his employees to deceive him. 'I just think they realised from the times I went down there that I preferred to keep it quiet for the time being and they kindly went along with the idea.'

'As it turned out, it may have been better if they hadn't.'

'Well, how was I to know Bevan would suddenly behave as he did? *You* were the one who suggested him as a teacher ... after making it plain you had no intention of taking on the tedious role, of course!' she couldn't resist reminding with a touch of acrimony.

Dev's head tilted as he eyed her askance. 'You claimed you weren't interested!'

'So what was I supposed to say when my husband had just shown all too clearly that he'd rather spend his time with my cousin?' She paused, grimacing sardonically. 'Even Bevan noticed that, you might remember! And what's more, you sure didn't deny it either, did you?'

'Since I didn't consider it worthy of a denial, why in hell should I? In any case, I was under the impression the less contact you had with me the better you liked it! Whenever I've suggested you join us you can't wait to refuse!'

Because it's always an invitation to join you *and* Adele, never just to go with *you* alone! she cried inwardly. Outwardly, however, pride had her schooling her features into showing no such torment. After all, he'd as good as admitted he preferred Adele's company with his first contention that he hadn't considered a denial of his interest was merited.

'Oh, well, that's the way it goes at times, I suppose,' she managed to force out with feigned unconcern in spite of the knot of misery lodged solidly in her chest. 'While on the subject of joining people, though, it's probably time we also adjourned to the dining room. By now, doubtlessly Adele will be most anxiously, not to say impatiently, awaiting *someone's* appearance at least.' With which lightly caustic observation she began heading for the door.

If he picked up the inference, Dev didn't remark on it but followed her silently for a time. 'And your riding? Do you want to continue with it?' he asked at length.

Meaning, he would arrange to foist her on to someone else if she so desired? 'I don't really know,' she shrugged. 'Not surprisingly, perhaps, it seems to have lost some of its appeal for the moment.' It hadn't at all, in truth, but since she already had a good grounding in the basics she saw no reason why she shouldn't continue practising on her own—and in private.

'Well, let me know what you decide and I'll see what can be arranged.'

So she was right! He did intend to push her on to somebody else! How utterly generous and considerate of him! Nodding her acknowledgment—she really didn't trust herself to speak—Raina preceded him into the dining room in something less than an affable frame of mind.

CHAPTER EIGHT

IN fact, the same mood remained with Raina for the whole of that day and the best part of the next—only replaced intermittently with an aching despair on seeing Adele continuing to treat Dev almost as if he was *her* husband, and him doing nothing to rectify the situation—so she was definitely in no humour to deal carefully, or even particularly civilly, with her cousin when she sauntered into the office where Raina was working the following afternoon.

'So this is where you've been hiding,' Adele drawled in a disparaging fashion, helping herself to a cigarette from the polished box on the desk and applying a flame to its tip from the lighter nearby before sinking serenely on to the chair facing Raina. 'I've been looking for you for almost half an hour.'

'Why? Has Dev managed to give you the slip for once?' Blue eyes connected satirically with brown.

Adele uttered an umused and completely confident little laugh. 'Now, now, darling, don't be catty,' she chided. 'You know as well as I do that he's not the slightest bit interested in giving *me* the slip.'

Knowing that it wasn't, unfortunately, a claim she could deny had Raina reacting irritably. 'Oh, go to blazes, Adele! Or better still, go back to Adelaide where you belong! In case you haven't guessed, you've worn out your welcome!'

'Not with Dev, I haven't,' the older girl smiled, unperturbed, and sent a smoke ring spiralling towards the ceiling. 'Although I can understand you saying it, of course. When all's said and done, you're on the verge of losing everything.'

'The only thing I'm on the verge of losing is my patience!' retorted Raina, refusing to give her the satisfaction of showing just *how* apprehensive she really was. 'And just maybe the only reason Dev hasn't also informed you your presence is becoming a pain is because he's trying to be polite!'

'I'm glad you said "just maybe" because we both know that isn't true, don't we?' countered Adele with insufferable self assurance. 'If it was, he'd no doubt be showing *you* over the property instead of *asking* me to accompany him all the time.' Pausing, her eyes started to shine with a taunting light. 'So perhaps it's you who's worn out their welcome, darling. Have you ever thought of that?'

'Hardly!' Raina made a valiant effort to laugh scornfully, although she suspected it was more of a strangled than a mirthful sound. 'You're simply mistakenly assuming everybody else falls out of love— and their marriages—with the same capriciousness and rapidity as you do!'

'Love! You and Dev?' Adele scoffed. 'Don't be ridiculous! Your occasional, supposedly amorous exchanges never fooled me for a minute!' She took a long draw on her cigarette before continuing in the same derisive vein. 'No, I've known—as has the whole family, naturally—why you married Dev from the moment we first received advice of the event, and if I needed any more proof, well . . . it's easy to see whose company Dev prefers, and that doesn't exactly constitute marital devotion, now does it? I mean, okay so you made a good attempt to thwart the rest of the family—although goodness only knows why Dev would have agreed to it—but unfortunately for you its failed completely and, quite frankly, I can't see what you hope to gain by continuing with the farce.' She took another draw on her cigarette. 'Indeed, if I were in your place, I'd be too embarrassed to keep trying to hang on to someone who so obviously wasn't interested in me, and would apply for a divorce as soon as I possibly could . . . as I'm sure you'd like to do too, if you would only admit it!'

'*You?* Embarrassed?' It was Raina's opportunity to mock now, electing to bypass her cousin's more contentious remarks. 'That'll be the day! You forget I've seen you in action before, Adele, and when it comes to getting what you want, embarrassment has never even had a place in your behaviour! To wit, your total lack of it in deliberately setting out to break up my marriage, and your insistence on remaining here, even though you were uninvited, for as long as you have. Besides,' she went on with a not altogether assumed confidence as a sudden recollection came to mind, 'Dev would never agree to a divorce, in any case. He, apparently, doesn't see them in quite the same light as you do, and he was most specific on the point before we were married.'

'That was also before he and I came to know each other better,' rejoined Adele with no visible decrease in her own self assurance. 'Not that it really matters, anyway, because once I've reported to Steven just what the true situation is here, I've no doubt he'll be able to use the information to prevent your scheme for stopping the Estate's sale. While as for Dev himself, well, although I find him exceedingly attractive, I've no wish to bury myself in the outback for the rest of *my* life, so once our affair has run its course I'll have no objection to handing him back to you if you're determined to continue with this charade of yours.'

Affair! The word struck at Raina with a lacerating, devastating force. Had their relationship really progressed to such an extent, or was her cousin merely implying it had to further her own ends? She was certainly calculating enough to do so, Raina knew, but at the same time she could also recall Dev once having declared that he also found Adele a very attractive woman. Suddenly, an unexpected knock on the door broke in on her dismal reverie and on glancing towards it she discovered Joe to be standing in the opening, his expression uncomfortably apologetic.

'I'm sorry to interrupt you, but . . .' he began.

'You don't have to apologise. Come right in,' Adele took it upon herself to reply as if it was her personal domain. 'I was just about to leave, anyway.' Stubbing out her cigarette she rose smoothly to her feet. 'Do keep in mind all I've had to say, though, won't you, Raina? I wouldn't want you laboring under any misapprehensions.' She smiled meaningfully down at the younger girl before taking her leave in the same ambling fashion as she had arrived.

With her departure, Raina pushed a supposedly calm half smile on to her lips and switched her attention to the lean, drill-clad overseer. 'Is there something I can do for you, Joe?'

He didn't immediately say, but with one last measuring glance after Adele, countered gruffly instead, 'I reckon there's plenty you should be doing for yourself where that one's concerned. That is, if your marriage really does mean anything to you.'

'And you think it doesn't?' Her eyes clouded sadly.

'No, as it happens, I think it's come to mean a great deal to you, if you must know,' he contradicted heavily.

Notwithstanding her surprise that he'd deduced so much, Raina felt a spurt of relief flash through her. Somehow Joe's approval had always seemed important to her. 'Unfortunately, however, it doesn't appear the same can be said of Dev since he now obviously finds other company more acceptable than mine,' she sighed.

'Mmm, but then, which came first? Him turning to her . . . or you turning him away?' Joe's tone held his meaning.

She hunched away from the too shrewd probing restively. 'I—well—all right, I admit I'm not altogether blameless, but as he's evidently made his choice there doesn't seem much I can do about it.'

Joe shook his head censuringly. 'Never did I think to see the day when a child of Hayes Cameron would turn out to be a quitter!' he condemned. 'Of course you can do something about it! For a start, it's time you stopped generously allowing Miss Arrogance to go off riding alone with him every morning. From what I hear via the grapevine you're competent enough in that regard these days to join them.'

'Oh, no, I'm sure I'm not,' Raina disputed. 'And I can't see it helping me at all by providing Adele the chance to make fun of the mistakes I do make in Dev's presence.'

'Not even if also gives you the opportunity to monopolise most of his time and attention by requesting his help in overcoming whatever problems—real, or—umm—invented—you may be experiencing?'

She couldn't help but laugh. 'You know, I've always thought of you as being as straight as a die, Joe Tierney, but now I'm beginning to realise there's more to you than meets the eye. You're not above being devious either when it suits you,' she charged.

A rueful smile crossed his own lips. 'Sometimes the only way to fight fire, is with fire. I just figure this is one of those times. In any event, isn't it also time you showed there's more to *you* as well than what Dev's seen so far?'

'Hmm . . .' Her features sobered thoughtfully. 'But

what if he isn't interested in rectifying any such—er—
riding deficiencies?'

'You really think he's not likely to?' It was obvious
Joe didn't.

'I suppose I *could* give it a try,' she mused,
weakening.

'You may be surprised by the results . . . especially if
you were to also show him that pretty smile of yours
more often.'

One such caught at her mobile mouth in response.
'That, as they would say in the cities nowadays, is sexist
talk, Joe.'

'I wouldn't know about that,' he shrugged with
evident indifference, 'I'm only a simple bushman, as
I've always said, but one thing I do know is that the old
saying that you'll catch more flies with honey than you
will with vinegar still holds true, no matter what fancy
label they want to put on it!'

'Then to prove I'm no quitter, I suppose I'll just have
to give it a go, won't I?' Raina proposed drily.

'You've nothing to lose, as I see it, but everything to
gain, lass,' he nodded.

'And that settled, now what can I do for you?' Her
brows arched enquiringly.

'Oh, since I was passing I just thought I'd see if
there had been any notification yet as to when that
polythene piping we ordered would be arriving?' he
advised.

She shook her head regretfully. 'No, not as yet, I'm
afraid.'

'Oh, well, they'd probably have trouble getting it on
the plane with all those wedding presents of yours,
anyway,' he bantered lightly.

'There's certainly been a few of them,' she acceded
with a rather ironically selfconscious half smile. In view
of the way her marriage had deteriorated she'd begun to

feel as if she was accepting them very much under false pretences.

About to leave, Joe glanced back at her from the doorway. 'A point you might do well to keep in mind though, lass, when you say Dev's made his choice, is that he *chose* to marry *you* . . . remember? And that has to mean something, doesn't it?' he contended implicitly as he departed.

Yes, it meant something, Raina allowed despondently. It meant her husband had been expecting a normal married relationship in return for his having taken on the added responsibility of managing the Estate's properties. Only she, of course, had stubbornly, stupidly, refused to permit that to eventuate, so that now . . . Now he had taken up her initial offer to pursue his social life as he pleased, and she only had herself to blame!

Whether or not she could reverse the situation, Raina really had no idea, but with Joe's promptings to urge her on she became more and more resolved as the day drew to a close to at least try. Pretending to an indifference she certainly didn't feel definitely hadn't improved matters, so as Joe had also implied, it surely couldn't make things any worse.

With her decision thus made, Raina set about shedding her usual distant and unconcerned attitude towards Dev and her cousin during dinner that evening, and replacing it with what her former friends and acquaintances would have regarded as her customary cheerful and vivacious good humour. Her efforts were rewarded to some degree by Dev, in turn, displaying more attention to her than he had for some considerable time—still rather reserved though it was—and much to Adele's evident dissatisfaction understandably, she was gratified to note.

Her success, coupled with Joe's surreptitiously

encouraging smile, gave her the confidence to further determine to approach her husband later when he returned to his room, and Adele would therefore be absent, to see if she couldn't bring about some sort of reconciliation, or at least an additional lowering of the barriers that had been raised between them.

When the opportunity presented itself, however, Raina discovered all her carefully rehearsed lines had suddenly deserted her, and it took some long, nerve-racking minutes for her to again pluck up sufficient courage to actually move across the room to their connecting door and raise her hand in preparation to knocking on it. With her knuckles a mere inch or so away from the wooden panelling, she abruptly jerked them away once more on hearing voices emanating from the other side. One voice in particular, an all too familiar, feminine voice, sounding more clearly and sending her emotions plummeting to the depths of wretched misery.

'Darling, I thought the evening would never pass,' Adele's impassioned words stabbed at her agonisingly. 'You must realise by now that we can't continue like this much longer. You know how I feel about you, so really isn't it time you told Raina your marrying her was all a ghastly mistake, and that you don't want her around any more?'

With a choking sob Raina clamped her hands over her ears and whirled away from the door, dreading to hear Dev concur with her cousin's suggestion. So Adele had been speaking the truth that afternoon. They were having an affair! And not only that, but they were so indifferent to her feelings that they were brazenly conducting it in the very next room to hers! she despaired brokenly.

Momentarily, all she could do was stand trembling with shock and distress in the middle of the room as her mind spun chaotically. So what did she do now? Confront them in outrage? No, she couldn't do that, she shrank away from the idea embarrassedly. Adele wouldn't be humiliated in the least by such an action, she knew, and as for Dev ... well, he could simply claim he was doing as she had recommended. No, the only person to be mortified by her bursting in on them would undoubtedly be herself!

But then, neither could she continue as if nothing had happened, she realised helplessly. Just knowing her presence was unwanted, or worse still, having Dev tell her so, was more than she could bear ... and so was the thought of remaining where she was while they made love in the very next room! That she didn't need! What she did want was peace and comfort, and from her subconscious seemed to come the immediate answer—Alliance and Ngarla. The urge to see the woman who had so often provided solace for her as a child suddenly strengthened overwhelmingly, and only pausing long enough to pull on a lacy cardigan over the dress she had worn to dinner in deference to the now cooling night-time temperatures, she was soon hurrying down the stairs and out of the homestead.

Deciding on the Land Cruiser as her best means of transport, Raina presently had it moving past the stockmen's quarters to a noisy accompaniment from the aroused dogs, but ignoring them, as well as the few lights their din succeeded in bringing on, she increased the pressure of her foot on the accelerator and swiftly left them all behind.

Due to the road having been newly graded all the way to Alliance now, Raina made far better time than had been the case on the first occasion Dev had driven her over, but it was still after one in the morning when she eventually pulled up in front of the mud-brick and stone house, once again to the unrestrained clamour of alert dogs.

For a second or two she experienced a twinge of guilt for having impulsively arrived at such an hour, but when the verandah light abruptly flashed on to reveal Ngarla, housecoat-covered and peering curiously into the darkness, she nevertheless flew towards her in relief, the numbed state of suspension that had sustained her throughout her journey at last dissolving beneath a flood of desolate tears as soon as she was enclosed within that woman's welcoming arms.

Three-quarters of an hour, plus copious cups of tea as well as a few cigarettes, later, Raina's whole story had been falteringly divulged—and been given a mixed reception. Although the soul of sympathy when she considered it was deserved, Ngarla also wasn't above failing to mince her words either when she believed the circumstances warranted it. In much the same manner she had summarily shooed Daniel back to bed as well when he too made an appearance to discover what all the commotion was about, although in his case, Raina suspected his willingness to do as his wife instructed had been caused more by the knowledge that he would still need to rise with the birds a few hours later than for any other reason.

Despite offering more compassion than criticism during Raina's narration, however, Ngarla remained obstinately unreceptive to the assertion that Dev had been unfaithful—due apparently to her unshakeable conviction that she had known him too long, and too well, to ever believe him capable of breaking any vow, let alone a marriage one—and no matter what evidence she produced Raina couldn't persuade her otherwise, somewhat to her dissatisfaction and resentment. It was all very well Ngarla not wanting to condemn him wrongly, but *she* knew it to be the truth!

They were still sitting in the kitchen discussing the

matter when, a short time later, the dogs again set up their barking and, glancing across the table, Raina gave a rueful half smile. 'What now, I wonder?'

Rising to her feet in order to go and find out once more, Ngarla's responding smile was wider, and even a touch wry. 'At a guess, I'd say it was your husband.'

A supposition that had Raina's expression rapidly turning to one of dismay. 'But it can't be!' she expostulated in something close to panic. 'How could he possibly know I'm here, or—even that I've left the homestead for that matter?'

'Your dogs *didn't* bark when you left?' quizzed Ngarla significantly before disappearing through the doorway.

Oh, God, of course they had! And if she hadn't been in such a distraught state she probably would have realised when those lights in the men's quarters had come on that *someone* would investigate the cause! Gaining her own feet now, she nervously made her way into the hall, but carefully ensuring she couldn't be seen from outside where, to her increasing agitation, another vehicle was indeed coming to a halt. One glimpse of the tall, powerfully built figure emerging from it sufficient to have her legs starting to shake uncontrollably.

'Now what would you be wanting at this hour, Dev?' called Ngarla with a hint of whimsical innocence from the verandah as he approached the steps.

'I've come to collect my wife ... as if you didn't know!' he returned in a drily expressive drawl. 'She is here, I see.' With a nod of his head to indicated the Land Cruiser.

'She's here,' was the laconic confirmation. 'Although not particularly anxious to see you at present, unless I'm mistaken.'

'I'm not surprised in view of the way she took off without warning in the middle of the night!'

From having been wishing she could just disappear, Raina now felt a new emotion abruptly sweep through her. Pure fury! That he had the audacity to complain about the manner in which she'd left, after the way he'd behaved was just too much! Flicking on the sitting room light, she waited wrathfully for them both to reach her.

'Annoyed because I ruined your cosily planned evening, are you?' she jeered immediately he did so, her blue eyes flashing. 'Well, isn't that a shame! Although you needn't have bothered to come to *collect* me,' with seething emphasis, 'because I don't intend to go anywhere with you ever again!'

'We'll see about that!' Dev rapped back, his very proximity making her edge into the sitting room before him. 'And, yes, I'm annoyed you ruined my evening! I had planned on trying to talk some sense into you!'

'Oh, how thoughtful!' she gritted facetiously. 'I was to be fitted in some time after you'd finished enjoying yourself with Adele, was I?'

'Enjoying myself with Adele?' His brows snapped together in a frown. 'What the hell's that supposed to mean?'

'She believes you're having an affair with her cousin,' put in Ngarla obligingly from where she was still standing near the doorway.

'What?' He turned to stare at the dark skinned woman incredulously. 'That's absurd!'

'Is it?' countered Raina in bitter accents. She arched a winged brow caustically as their glances clashed again. 'That door between our rooms isn't exactly soundproof, you know! Or was that the idea ... for me to hear the pair of you in there together?'

A look of dawning apprehension swept over his good-looking face and an oblique tilt caught his mouth sideways as he began to nod. 'So that's what's at the bottom of all this, is it?'

'There! I told you!' It was Raina who turned to Ngarla now, outwardly triumphant, but inwardly devastated. 'You notice he didn't deny it!'

'Because there's nothing to deny, of course!' Dev retorted dismissively. He paused, eyeing her with a kind of taunting speculation. 'Although even if there had been, I'm not sure why you should object quite so— er—fervently. After all, it was you who suggested I could . . . shall we say, find my pleasures wherever I pleased?'

Raina bit at her lower lip anguishedly. 'But—but . . .'

'That was before she realised she was in love with you,' inserted a soft voice.

'*Ngarla!*' The strangled cry burst from Raina in horrified reproach.

The housekeeper merely smiled and nodded—in confirmation of an expressively raised brow from Dev, Raina noted in part anger, part despair, feeling as if she'd been sold out—and proposed, 'Now having said that, which should help explain a lot of things, I'll leave you two to finally settle matters in private. Good night.' Almost out of the room, she glanced back over her shoulder. 'Oh, yes, you can use the main bedroom, and I'll see you in the morning.'

Her parting suggestion brought a lazy smile to Dev's lips but a dismayed choking sound to Raina's. How could Ngarla have betrayed her so completely! Only Ngarla wasn't her immediate problem now, her husband was, she realised with a gulp on seeing him closing the gap between them with a slow, deliberate stride.

'So is it true?' he probed softly on coming to a halt mere inches in front of her.

Raina nervously ran the tip of her tongue over her lips, feeling more defenceless and uncertain of herself than she ever had in her life before, and wishing irrelevantly that he didn't look quite so invincible . . . quite so damned undeniably attractive!

'N-no, of course not!' she lied desperately, finding her voice at last, and trying to increase the distance between then again by taking a few hasty steps backwards—until one side of the arch leading into the dining room disconcertingly halted her progress. 'She—she's confused something I said evidently, or—or perhaps she just mis-heard me.' She took a deep, jagged breath and tenaciously injected some conviction back into her voice. 'But whatever, you needn't think I'm about to conveniently take Adele's place just because you unaccountably felt obliged to interrupt your pleasurable evening with her!'

'Pleasurable!' he surprised her by half laughing derisively. 'As you should know, sweetheart, time spent with your cousin may be many things, but pleasurable it very definitely is not! And for your information,' a swift movement of his hand suddenly had her rebellious face tipping upwards, 'she wasn't in my room this evening at my invitation, and nor was she there very long. *I* saw to that!'

'Yeah, I can just picture it!' she sniped acidly, twisting her chin free of his hold but continuing to hold it at an antagonistic angle. 'Particularly after I heard what she had to say about the pair of you not being able to continue as you were any longer, and how it was time for you to tell me I wasn't wanted any more!'

'And did you also hear what I said in reply?'

'What do you think I am, a masochist? No, I didn't stop to hear any more, I'd already heard more than enough, thanks!' She had to blink quickly to dispel the sting of salt beneath her eyelids, then shook her head wearily. 'So why don't you just admit it's the truth and be done with it!'

Strangely, depressingly, that had the beginnings of a

slow smile easing across his well shaped mouth. 'Would you recognise, or believe, the truth if you heard it?' he quizzed in a wry drawl, stroking a forefinger tantalisingly across her suddenly warming cheek.

'I've already d-done so,' she maintained on a shaky note.

'Uh-uh,' he contradicted laconically, his whole hand caressing the side of her neck now, and causing her heart to react in a traitorous fashion by responding with an almost delirious hammering. 'Because you see, there never could have been anything between Adele and me due to my heart already having been well and truly captured previously by a very beautiful, if at times damnable contrary, but still utterly bewitching young girl whose father I liked and respected from the moment I met him . . . but whose daughter I think I fell in love with at first sight.'

Raina swallowed with difficulty, her eyes rounding in disbelief. He was meaning *her*! Oh, if only it were true! 'You're just saying that in order to divert my attention from . . .'

'I only wish I could,' Dev interposed drily and set his mouth to hers persuasively, his lips moving against her own in a firm yet gentle, but continuing caress that, as always, had her own lips waywardly returning the stimulating pressure.

Except for the hand that was still cupping her neck, their mouths were their only point of contact, but on finding herself compulsively swaying towards him, seeking a closer encounter, Raina gave a gasp and frantically jerked away from him altogether.

'No!' she protested breathlessly. 'You and Adele . . .'

'Me and Adele, *nothing*!' Dev broke in on her, a hard note entering his voice. 'And after what I had to say to her tonight, probably less than that, if that's possible! She's been nothing but a bloody pain in the neck ever since she arrived, and if she does as I suggested and packs her bags tonight, no one will be happier to see the last of her than I will, believe me!'

He sounded genuine enough, and yet ... 'And why would you do that?' Raina questioned sceptically.

'Partly because she stretches goodwill to its absolute limits like I've never known anyone do before, but mainly—and as inconceivable as it apparently seems to you—I take extremely strong exception to females who think they can wander into my room at will with amorous propositions I'm not the least interested in, nor for which I offered any encouragement, and then dare to presume to recommend that, (a), I should cheat on my wife who I happen to love very deeply, and who I can only pray might one day feel the same about me, and (b), having done that, then proceed to suggest I inform her that I don't want her around any more, when that's precisely what I *do* want!' he ground out in rasping tones. Pausing, he dragged a hand through his hair irritably before going on in a somewhat hoarse tone. 'In the name of heaven, Raina, why in blazes did you think I agreed to marry you in the first place? You must have known a share in your family's estate, nor the increased land holdings meant much to me. *You* were the only part of that deal to hold any interest for me!'

In spite of her heart pounding so rapidly she thought it would burst, Raina still had to charge, 'Well, you certainly never appeared to have any objections when you were with her, and—and *she* was the one you took with you all the time!' The last with distinctly more than a hint of resentment.

Dev's mouth quirked with a brief flash of mocking humour. 'Of course I took her with me whenever I possibly could! With a scheming, trouble-making cat like that around she would've made your life hell, and doubtlessly torn you to pieces in the process, if I'd left her alone with you all the time! I simply considered it the best way to curtail her activities as far as you were concerned, while hopefully also distracting her attention.' He gave a low, vibrant, but regretful laugh. 'Although definitely not in the manner it turned out!'

So it had all been on her own behalf—and she had done nothing but mentally castigate him for it! Shamefaced, she couldn't quite meet his dark gaze as she questioned in a small voice, 'Then why didn't you tell me that was the reason behind it? I thought—I thought . . .'

A hand ensnaring her chin again and tilting her face up to his had her breaking off, the smile slowly widening his mouth warm and captivating in its effect, making her pulse race erratically. 'Hmm, it's become very obvious what you thought, my doubting, provoking, little love,' he drawled lazily. 'But if you will recall, it's been somewhat difficult to get you to even speak to me at all—well, for any longer than a couple of minutes at least—for some time now.'

'I'm sorry.' Her blue eyes shaded contritely. Then, with a half feigned grimace of reproach as a sudden recollection occurred, 'Although you were also quick to suspect me of encouraging Bevan, as I remember!'

'For which *I'm* very sorry,' he apologised deeply. 'But when you admitted you'd been meeting him secretly . . .' He sighed and shook his head ruefully.

'At least I did give you an explanation for that later. You refused to with regard to your apparent interest in Adele. You just said it wasn't worthy of any comment.'

'And nor was it as far as I was concerned since it was so untrue, and so unlikely, to even be contemplated! Oh, kitten,' he cupped her face between his palms, his tone thickening, 'how could it possibly have been otherwise with you around?'

The warmth in his voice had her feeling weak in the legs but still she had to remind him, 'You did say once that you considered her a very attractive woman, though.'

'As she is . . . on the outside!' The scornful twist to his lips left in her no doubt as to what he thought of her cousin as a whole. 'Besides, at the time I rather suspect that was merely said in return for a remark you'd just made.'

'Oh?'

'Mmm, if I remember correctly, you implied I was flattered by her attentions,' he relayed with a mock ferocious glower. 'Which, of course, I very definitely wasn't . . . especially in view of the fact that the only member of your family I wanted interested in me was you!'

'Oh, Dev!' Raina reached up to link her arms about his neck adoringly. 'I do love you, I honestly do . . . just as Ngarla said! And so very, very much!'

Crushing her to him, Dev's lips found hers unerringly, her response ready and unstinting. 'I also think Ngarla must have known something when she recommended the main bedroom for us tonight,' he breathed unsteadily long moments later as he swept her high into his arms and began heading down the hall.

Raina leant her head against his broad chest contentedly, her eyes slumbrous as they remained fastened lovingly to his manly, sun-darkened features. 'You once said you weren't interested in sharing a bed with me,' she murmured teasingly as he shouldered open the door to the softly lamp-lit bedroom. More of Ngarla's handiwork, she immediately mused inconsequentially.

Pushing the door closed behind them with his foot, Dev halted, his shapely mouth taking on a lazily provoking curve. 'You also once claimed it would only be under duress that you'd share one with me.'

'Except that I've already made a liar of myself with that statement by doing precisely that on our wedding night,' she recalled a trifle selfconsciously.

'Mmm, but then I also suspected that was merely a form of release for other emotions,' he revealed on a wry note.

She nodded. 'So did I at the time. But now,' she dimpled engagingly, 'I'm beginning to wonder if it wasn't just a case of my heart knowing what I wanted even if my head was refusing to admit it.' She paused, slanting him a provocative look from beneath glossy lashes. 'However, if you're still of the same opinion about not wanting to sleep with me . . .'

'You believe that and you'll believe anything!' he growled huskily, carrying her swiftly across to the wide bed.

Awakening langorously the following morning, Raina remained still for a time as memories of their impassioned lovemaking of the hours before flooded back to her, and relishing the feel of Dev's hard muscled form as it lay pressed against hers. She had never known such pleasure and the thought of their continuing life together filled her with an overwhelming elation.

Beside her Dev stirred, and turning her head on her pillow to look at him, found him watching her lazily. 'Happy?' he asked softly.

'Unbelievably,' she smiled. 'And you?'

He drew her even closer within his strong, encircling arms. 'How could I fail to be with someone as lovable and so very delightful as you for my wife?'

Raina moved to place a lingering kiss on his smoothly muscular shoulder. 'Not that you always appeared to think that way, of course,' she charged, her mouth shaping mischievously. 'In fact, you were so horribly disparaging that day at the funeral that I can't really believe you fell in love with me at *first* sight.'

'I was, wasn't I?' he grinned without the slightest sign of remorse and had her eyeing him in pretended indignation. 'But having already reached the conclusion that I would dislike you, anyway, for having been as callous towards Hayes as I believed you'd been, I then wasn't exactly overjoyed to find myself considerably more than a little attracted to you notwithstanding.'

'While I thought you were the most arrogant, interfering, and positively infuriating man on earth,' she disclosed in laughing retaliation.

'It was still *your* idea for us to marry,' he taunted. 'As I reminded you when you offered to leave in Bevan's place that day.'

So that was what he'd meant by saying since she'd made her bed, she could then lie in it! Considering where she was right at the moment, she could smile about it now, and did so as she replied no less goadingly, 'I must have been mad!'

An abrupt movement had him suddenly leaning over her, his eyes narrowing in supposed menace. 'Would you care to repeat that?' he challenged.

'I said, I must have been mad!' she dared to defy with a chuckle. Then, sliding her hands up to frame his face, added with quiet fervour, 'Not to have realised that I wasn't entirely unaware of you even then.'

He smiled, his mouth descending to hers and remaining there for some long, leisurely minutes. 'You keep saying things like that, wife, and we may not leave this bed all day,' he forecast throatily.

Wife! On his lips it sounded the most satisfying word she had ever heard. 'And if we didn't, do you think Adele may take the hint and have departed from Ajax

Downs before we return?' she put forward somewhat shyly.

'We can always hope!'

'She'll still try and make trouble, though, once she gets in touch with Steven,' she sighed.

'She'll have a damn sight more trouble attempting to convince anyone we didn't marry for love after this,' Dev half laughed expressively, beginning to ease her beneath him.

That she certainly would, smiled Raina with satisfaction before casting all further thoughts of her cousin aside as she began to respond to her husband's passionate lips and caressing hands with increasing rapture. From now on she knew no one would ever again be able to doubt that most tender of emotions was absent from their marriage.

She just hoped that, somehow, maybe her father would also know, and rest content in the knowledge that his daughter had returned to share her life with the man he had called friend, and on the land he too had loved so deeply.

ROMANCE

Next month's romances from Mills & Boon

Each month, you can choose from a world of variety in romance with Mills & Boon. These are the new titles to look out for next month.

FINDING OUT Lindsay Armstrong
ESCAPE ME NEVER Sara Craven
POINT OF IMPACT Emma Darcy
SILENT CRESCENDO Catherine George
THE MAN IN ROOM 12 Claudia Jameson
THE HARD MAN Penny Jordan
HUNGER Rowan Kirby
A LAKE IN KYOTO Marjorie Lewty
PALE ORCHID Anne Mather
NEVER THE TIME AND THE PLACE Betty Neels
*****LEGACY** Doris Rangel
*****FOREVER** Lynn Turner

Buy them from your usual paperback stockist, or write to: Mills & Boon Reader Service, P.O. Box 236, Thornton Rd, Croydon, Surrey CR9 3RU, England. Readers in South Africa - write to: Mills & Boon Reader Service of Southern Africa, Private Bag X3010, Randburg, 2125.

*These two titles are available *only* from Mills & Boon Reader Service.

Mills & Boon
the rose of romance

Take 4
Exciting Books
Absolutely
FREE

Love, romance, intrigue... all are captured for you by Mills & Boon's top-selling authors. By becoming a regular reader of Mills & Boon's Romances you can enjoy 6 superb new titles every month plus a whole range of special benefits: your very own personal membership card, a free monthly newsletter packed with recipes, competitions, exclusive book offers and a monthly guide to the stars, plus extra bargain offers and big cash savings.

**AND an Introductory FREE GIFT for YOU.
Turn over the page for details.**

As a special introduction we will send you four exciting Mills & Boon Romances Free and without obligation when you complete and return this coupon.

At the same time we will reserve a subscription to Mills & Boon Reader Service for you. Every month, you will receive 6 of the very latest novels by leading Romantic Fiction authors, delivered direct to your door. You don't pay extra for delivery — postage and packing is always completely Free. There is no obligation or commitment — you can cancel your subscription at any time.

You have nothing to lose and a whole world of romance to gain.

Just fill in and post the coupon today to **MILLS & BOON READER SERVICE, FREEPOST, P.O. BOX 236, CROYDON, SURREY CR9 9EL.**

Please Note:- **READERS IN SOUTH AFRICA write to Mills & Boon, Postbag X3010, Randburg 2125, S. Africa.**

FREE BOOKS CERTIFICATE

To: Mills & Boon Reader Service, FREEPOST, P.O. Box 236, Croydon, Surrey CR9 9EL.

Please send me, free and without obligation, four Mills & Boon Romances, and reserve a Reader Service Subscription for me. If I decide to subscribe I shall, from the beginning of the month following my free parcel of books, receive six new books each month for £6.60, post and packing free. If I decide not to subscribe, I shall write to you within 10 days. The free books are mine to keep in any case. I understand that I may cancel my subscription at any time simply by writing to you. I am over 18 years of age.

Please write in BLOCK CAPITALS.

Signature _____

Name _____

Address _____

_____ Post code _____

SEND NO MONEY — TAKE NO RISKS.

Please don't forget to include your Postcode.

Remember, postcodes speed delivery. Offer applies in UK only and is not valid to present subscribers. Mills & Boon reserve the right to exercise discretion in granting membership. If price changes are necessary you will be notified.

6R   Offer expires 31st December 1985

EP8

ROMANCE

Variety is the spice of romance

Each month, Mills & Boon publish new romances. New stories about people falling in love. A world of variety in romance — from the best writers in the romantic world. Choose from these titles in November.

RETURN TO WALLABY CREEK Kerry Allyne
PILLOW PORTRAITS Rosemary Carter
THE DRIFTWOOD DRAGON Ann Charlton
TO CAGE A WHIRLWIND Jane Donnelly
A MAN WORTH KNOWING Alison Fraser
INJURED INNOCENT Penny Jordan
TOUCH NOT MY HEART Leigh Michaels
SWEET AS MY REVENGE Susan Napier
SOUTH SEAS AFFAIR Kay Thorpe
DANGER ZONE Madeleine Ker
*__THE GARLAND GIRL__ Liza Manning
*__MacBRIDE OF TORDARROCH__ Essie Summers

On sale where you buy paperbacks. If you require further information or have any difficulty obtaining them, write to: Mills & Boon Reader Service, PO Box 236, Thornton Road, Croydon, Surrey CR9 3RU, England.

*These two titles are available *only* from Mills & Boon Reader Service.

Mills & Boon
the rose of romance